**COMBAT**
**AND**
**SURVIVAL**
WHAT IT TAKES TO FIGHT AND WIN

VOLUME
15

Originally published in the United Kingdom in weekly parts **COMBAT & SURVIVAL** is a study of the armed forces at work. It shows the skills taught to soldiers and the way in which military units operate. It examines the weapons and equipment used by different armies; and, by looking at recruit training and exercises, **COMBAT & SURVIVAL** demonstrates how the armed forces develop individual responsibility, leadership and initiative.

# COMBAT AND SURVIVAL

### WHAT IT TAKES TO FIGHT AND WIN

## VOLUME
## 15

H. S. STUTTMAN INC. *Publishers*          Westport, Connecticut 06880

# Contents
## Volume 15

Published by H. S. STUTTMAN INC.
Westport, Connecticut 06889
© Aerospace Publishing 1991
ISBN 0-87475-560-3

4P(2295)20–90

# Combat Skills

# OBSERVING THE ENEMY

*In battle it's vital that you know as much as possible about the strength, movement, positions and intentions of the enemy. Modern warfare is highly mobile and technologically sophisticated, but commanders still acquire some of their best information from static observation posts (OPs) in carefully chosen sites, concealed from the enemy and manned by a few sharp-eyed infantrymen.* This section of the Combat Skills course concentrates on how to set up an OP, how to survive in its cramped conditions, and what to look out for when on watch.

In conventional warfare mobile OPs are provided either by the Scorpions and Scimitars of reconnaissance regiments and static OPs by infantry patrols. In counter-insurgency or internal security (IS) situations covert OPs are provided almost exclusively by the infantry.

## 1 Choosing the site

Obviously your OP must provide a good view over the ground that you want to watch. Therefore it should have as wide a field of view and as little dead ground as possible. This is as much for security as for observation – a small infantry OP does not want to be surprised by a larger enemy patrol. It should have a covered and safe approach and exit, and it should provide good cover from view and from fire. In order to achieve the latter, you will probably have to dig in, which should in any case help conceal you. The position should not, however, be an obvious choice for an OP site. The enemy is not a fool.

An OP party is not normally strong enough to take offensive action itself. However, in a conventional war situation it can bring down artillery or mortar fire, and in an IS situation it can direct a quick reaction force to the scene of the incident. Last, an OP site must permit excellent radio communications. It is no good an OP spotting some crucial enemy activity and being able to do nothing about it.

## 2 Occupying the OP

Once you have chosen your site (you may have to do this from a map or from air photographs), you will have to set about occupying it. First, the ground must be cleared to make sure there are no enemy in the vicinity and to make sure there are no booby traps around. Next, you must ensure that your communications are not affected by the location. You can only do this by calling your HQ from the OP itself. You may then need to dig trenches, which could take up to 24 hours, depending on the ground. It may not

*This Observation Post in South Armagh overlooks the border with the Irish Republic. This is a permanent OP, and is 'overt', i.e. not intended to be hidden, and is heavily fortified.*

be possible to move, let alone dig, during daylight hours so you could take two nights to complete your position.

Finally, you must prepare range cards. Look at your map and relate certain prominent objects to your own position in terms of range. This will prove an easy way of determining the range of another location quickly, by using the nearest reference point.

## Post routine

The most obvious factor that will affect the routine in the OP is the number of men you are able to take. While it is seldom necessary to have more than two men actually on duty in the OP at any one time, there is a limit to the length of time that a man can closely and continuously observe the same piece of ground. Most people's concentration fades after about 30 minutes. If you put two men on duty for two hours, they should alternate every 15 minutes.

To make life even more complicated everyone in the OP must be ready to move instantly. If there is a real danger of a very small OP party being discovered by a much larger group of enemy, discretion may be the better part of valour and a rapid withdrawal is advisable.

OP work, although it can pay enormous dividends, is usually boring. The only way you can guarantee that the job is done properly is to follow certain procedures. The man who is not observing should act as a sentry and observe the area around the OP. This can also be done by those in an administrative area if your OP is large enough to have one.

You must keep in touch by radio with your HQ, and you should do this at pre-arranged times – if only to

**Individual Weapon Sight (IWS)**
This is a first-generation image intensifier which amplifies the amount of light available. Because it simply makes better use of the available light it does not work well on a moonless night or in smoky conditions.

**IWS sight picture**
This is the sort of image you get from the IWS. It is very tiring on the eyes to peer through it, and ideally you should observe for no longer than 30 minutes before handing over to someone else in the OP. Here an arms cache is being unloaded at a deserted farmhouse. The magnification provided by IWS allows you to identify what sort of weapons the enemy are carrying.

**Close recce**
When it's very dark or there is a heavy morning mist or fog, you might have to carry out a close target recce. Choose a close recce position which you can cover by fire from the OP itself.

**Ready to move**
All kit should be ready to move at a moment's notice in case a quick bug-out is called for.

## Covert Observation Post

*Selection of the site for your observation post is absolutely critical. In wartime, the only aids available to you are a map and air photograph, but in counter-revolutionary warfare you may be able to visit and recce possible sites. However, do not rely on this: good appreciation of ground and being able to look at a map and 'see' the ground in your mind's eye is vital. You need to place your OP as far away from the target as is allowed by the nature of the target and your surveillance devices. On some occasions you may be over a kilometre away, while on others you may be right on the enemy's doorstep.*

**Sketch map**
You need a detailed sketch map of the area and an OP log kept of all significant events.

**Surveillance devices**
As well as binoculars and image intensifiers, thermal imaging, ground radar, intruder systems and seismic sensors are employed on OPs.

**M79 grenade launcher**
This single-shot, break-action 40-mm grenade launcher is accurate enough to get a grenade through a window at 150 metres. It can give you valuable edge.

report that nothing has happened. In this way HQ will know your position has not been compromised and that you are safe. Obviously you should send back important information as soon as you can.

## What to look for

You should split the area that you are observing into foreground, middle distance and background. In that way you can scan each part methodically and carefully with binoculars from one side to another. Rest your eyes at frequent intervals.

While you are searching the ground, you should look very carefully for anything that does not fit easily with its surroundings. Don't look for a tank, or a trench system. Look instead for an indication that might let you pinpoint a tank or a trench system. In other words, look for mistakes in enemy camouflage.

Look for foliage that is out of place or foliage which is withering for no

particular reason. Look for track marks or areas of ground that have been disturbed. Be suspicious if birds or animals are disturbed. Look for something glinting in the sun, look for a vehicle exhaust or a camp fire. You

*Changing stag (sentry duty) on a permanent OP on the Irish border. The OP commander briefs the man relieving him on his arcs of observation and responsibility.*

### Minimum strength
Four people is the minimum required for an OP; this sort of work is probably the most demanding infantry skill. It is physically cramped and exhausting, but you must remain alert all the time you are on duty. If your attention wanders for even a moment you may miss something vital and all your effort will have been for nothing.

### Light machine-gun
Automatic weapons are not essential on an OP, but they are a source of comfort. The LMG is more accurate and lighter than the GPMG and ideal for this sort of job.

### Summer Time factor
Be aware that short summer nights combined with a long patrol route in will not leave you long to build your OP. It may be necessary to construct your OP over two nights, camouflaging your work in the meantime.

### Shotgun
There is nothing like a 12-gauge pump-action shotgun for point-blank range firepower.

### Stags
Usually two people will be on duty at once: the observer and the sentry. The observer scans the target and notes down any activity while the sentry covers all approaches to the OP in case the position is compromised. The two men swap over functions when using surveillance devices, which are tiring on the eyes.

### Weapons
Weapons should be cocked and ready to hand at all times. Never clean more than one at once. A four-man OP is not intended to fight; it relies for defence on not being seen. You'll need a weapons mix to cover short and long range options.

# SITING YOUR OP

**1** An OP is essentially a type of patrol: here the four-man OP team, in diamond formation for crossing open ground at night, moves towards an OP site selected from maps, photos, and previous patrol reports.

**4** The patrol commander uses the linked legs to pass information. He sends the message on the left and receives it on the right, thus knowing that each member of the patrol has understood.

**7** As soon as the recce team moves off, the two men left at the FRV move round to cover 180° each. They recognise the patrol commander by pre-arranged signal when he returns from the OP site. Remember that this is all happening at night, in enemy territory.

**2** The patrol commander, having used his IWS to select a good FRV position, passes the message to the rest of the patrol.

**5** The OP recce: the OP commander and his radio operator move forward stealthily as a two-man team, covering each other. If compromised at this stage you have to use an alternative site.

**8** Another listening stop follows in the FRV before the whole team move out to occupy the OP position.

**3** The patrol occupies the FRV (Final Rendez Vous). This should be some distance from the actual OP position and should be easily recognisable at night. Note that in the FRV the patrol covers 360° and has a listening stop to make sure they are not followed.

**6** Next you recce the exact spot where you will site the OP. The patrol commander checks that he can actually see the target and that the OP has good all-round observation. The radio operator checks he is 'in comms' with HQ.

**9** The OP position: all four members take up their allotted places, cover their arcs and listen for the enemy. When the OP commander is satisfied that the enemy has not seen them move in, he gives the signal for 'packs off' and the team moves into the set-up phase.

should search dark areas with particular care. Above all, you should look for movement. It is movement more than anything else that will draw your attention towards an enemy vehicle, patrol or position.

In counter-insurgency operations you must have done your homework regarding terrorist recognition. There will be a 'rogue's gallery' that you will have studied in great depth so that you can instantly recognise a wanted man. You may also have to memorise car registration numbers. In a conventional operation you must be able to identify enemy armoured fighting vehicles (AFVs). The type of vehicle will often identify the type of enemy formation you are facing. This sort of information is invaluable for your HQ to build up an accurate intelligence picture. In the confusion of battle you must be sure that you do not wrongly identify and engage one of your own AFVs.

## Urban OPs

On internal security operations, you may need to set up your OP in an urban environment. Derelict or unoc-cupied houses or the roofs of apartment blocks can all be used. If you want to use a window for observation, net curtains are useful, but you must stand back from the window. If you are in an attic it is possible to move a tile a few inches so that you can look through. Unless you are situated on a high building most urban OPs will only provide a view down one or two streets but that is probably all that is necessary as it is usually a house or street that you wish to watch. Clearly the injection and extraction of this sort of OP will be much more difficult.

# THE SET-UP PHASE

*While the OP is being constructed, a sentry is placed on a flank at the limit of noise or vision, whichever is the further. He looks and listens for the enemy, who are hopefully blissfully unaware of the team's presence. Depending on the situation you may need to dig in, either to protect yourself from fire or to conceal yourself if your OP site is on open ground.*

**3** Meanwhile, the third man pulls the poncho and cam net out of his Bergen. The cam net has already been cut to size and is attached to the poncho. Remember to observe even while you are working, and do not sit or stand up above the level of the black screen.

**4** Next you put up the overhead cover, which keeps the rain off and camouflages the position. It must be camouflaged from the air as well as the ground.

**5** The poncho is now in place. You must attach the bungees before you start as you'll never find them at night otherwise. Commercially purchased DPM ponchos are best because they are bigger. Do not cut off any branches or disturb the undergrowth.

**6** The OP seen from the front without camouflage. At night it is movement which attracts the eye; you will only move behind your black screen.

**1** Armed with a Light Support Weapon, the sentry covers the OP team as they work. In a dug-in OP the work phase could be as long as six or seven hours, in which case sentry duty must be rotated.

**2** The OP commander and observer first put up a black hessian screen to work behind. This is secured to the cover with bungees. Remember this is at night, so you must practise beforehand.

**7** The rear of the OP, fully camouflaged. The cam net which is attached to the poncho should be large enough to fold down over all sides. The overall effect can be improved by the use of local camouflage, but don't cut it from right by the OP position. As it wilts it must be replaced.

**8** The front of the OP. Ideally if your position is correctly camouflaged, the only way the enemy should be able to find it is to tread on it.

**9** When observing, the observer pushes his head or his surveillance device underneath the black screen. Use of active surveillance devices must be kept to a minimum since they can easily be detected.

# Combat Report
## Vietnam:
## Standby Patrol in a Firefight

**Andrew Freemantle left the British Army in 1969 and served for three years with the Royal Australian Regiment and Australian Special Air Service. He served for 11 months in Vietnam.**

On 22 May 1971 I was commanding the standby patrol in the Australian SAS squadron base on the hill at Nui Dat, South Vietnam. The task of my five-man team on that day was to be prepared at short notice to deploy, by a variety of methods, either to reinforce or assist one of our patrols already in there.

One such patrol (call sign 23, a five-man recce patrol) had been operating for five days some 50 miles to the north of Nui Dat, in an American area usually patrolled by the 1st Air Cavalry and notorious for its high level of enemy activity.

On 21 May, patrol 23 had reported seeing and hearing some main force Viet Cong constructing bunkers in an area of thick secondary jungle. The patrol had attempted a close recce, but it had great difficulty getting very close to the enemy because large numbers of dried leaves on the ground made quiet movement almost impossible. But it was clear from the number of enemy seen, and the amount of general enemy movement in the area, that a significant position, possibly a battalion base, was being constructed.

### We were under fire

The commander of patrol 23 had decided to withdraw to a safer area and call for the assistance of a standby patrol. This would give him a better chance of being able to fight his way out if he got into trouble, or of being able to create a diversion should either patrol be compromised.

So on the morning of 22 May my patrol, patrol 15, abseiled through the trees to reinforce patrol 23, in an area far enough away from the enemy sighting to make it impossible for them to hear us. Various diversionary tactics were used to disguise the whereabouts of our helicopters, but because of the frequent chopper movements in much of South Vietnam (unlike previous jungle campaigns such as Malaya or Borneo) the use of helicopters to insert covert patrol was not as risky as it might seem.

Once on the ground we received an update of

**A UH-1D of the RAAF with an SAS patrol dangling underneath. In emergencies the helicopter could lower ropes rather than land.**

the situation. Then we patrolled carefully towards where patrol 23 had seen the enemy. This took several hours, but by 14.30 we were in the vicinity of the enemy camp. By this stage our rate of movement had slowed to about a hundred metres in an hour, and we were all acutely aware of an enemy presence, even though we'd not yet seen anyone.

Without warning a Viet Cong soldier, dressed in green and carrying an AK-47, appeared from behind a tree about five metres away and opened fire. By this time in the tour we were quite quick on the draw, so he flew back in a hail of fire from our automatic SLRs and M-16s.

Then all hell broke loose. Obviously we'd walked right into the middle of what appeared to be a major VC bunker complex. Within a few seconds we were under fire from six occupied bunkers, dug in an L-shaped configuration. We were forced to go to ground in a shallow depression about seven metres from the nearest bunker.

My patrol seemed to be under fire from three bunkers along the bottom of the L, and the patrol we'd been sent to reinforce was about 20 metres away, under fire from bunkers along the side of the L. The enemy, of course, were firing through slits in the front and sides of each bunker, so when we started to throw grenades at them they exploded harmlessly, either on the trench parapet or on top of the metre or so of overhead protection that formed the roof of each bunker.

But when the enemy threw grenades at us we had no such protection, and things became quite lively. Mick, my medic, was soon wounded in the shoulder and leg. I felt a great whoosh behind me and a stinging sensation in my backside. An enemy grenade had gone over our heads and exploded just behind us.

### We'd fired 200 rounds apiece

The ensuing fire fight lasted for about 20 minutes and was conducted at ranges of no more than 20 metres. I remember admiring the coolness of trooper Hans, already the holder of the DCM, firing deliberately and steadily at the muzzle flashes from the nearest bunker, while branches, leaves and wood chips thrown up by enemy fire flew all around him.

Meanwhile, I took stock of a rapidly deteriorating situation. The options were simple: either storm what was largely an unknown but well protected objective, or get the hell out of it and live to fight another day. I

**The intense helicopter activity meant that small patrols could be dropped off without too much risk of attracting enemy attention.**

decided on the latter course, and I must say it's a decision I have never regretted.

By this stage we'd all fired at least 200 rounds apiece, and thrown or fired most of our grenades. At this moment some bright spark fired a 40-mm CS gas cartridge at a bunker, and missed. But the resulting cloud of gas, together with white phosphorus smoke, created enough confusion to allow us to break contact, using individual fire and movement, crawling on our bellies and pulling our wounded.

### Everybody had withdrawn

In spite of the noise and confusion, my IC Clive, an ex-Royal Marine, had remembered to make ready a time-delay smoke container to mark the camp so that bombers could attack it later from the air. I watched with alarm as the hand on the watch of the timing device fell off as he put the smoke container down behind a tree. With great presence of mind he pulled out a knife, smashed the watch-glass with the handle, and carefully repositioned the hand. By this time everybody else had withdrawn, and I was rather keen to join them.

Twenty minutes later we reached a small clearing, and we were all extracted by winch, under cover of fire from helicopter gunships that suppressed the enemy throughout. Only one of us needed hospital treatment, and the rest of us needed a beer on our return to base.

**The enemy bunker complex. Their overhead cover made them safe from grenade attacks, and their narrow firing slits offered a poor target.**

# PREPARED FOR A LONG VIGIL

**Before you move out on the patrol that will put you into position in your OP, you must check your equipment and weapons.** Re-supply could compromise your position – a helicopter carrying spare batteries or even a patrol carrying ammunition or stores will attract attention if they are moving in a sensitive area.

Folding digging tools are essential to prepare the position, and a wire saw and secateurs will allow you to cut vegetation to clear viewing points through cover or to garnish the position. An axe or parang is less suitable, since chopping is a noisy business.

A small camouflage net to hang in the observation port, or light chicken wire to attach camouflage garnish are also useful: remember, the hole you look through at the enemy will look like a black hole in green vegetation unless you camouflage it.

## Stags of duty

Once you are in position you will need to work out the stags of duty. Two men on and two men off, staggered so that one man is fresh on as the other is half way through his stag, helps ensure that no-one falls asleep or loses concentration. Basic equipment that you need includes the prismatic compass for bearings on contacts and binoculars for detailed

*On stag, in an overt OP, training for Counter Revolutionary Warfare (CRW). As a rule, two people will be on duty at any one time. A high degree of concentration is required to remain alert for long periods: OP duty is the most demanding of all infantry skills.*

*Internal security OP in Ulster is shown here during the early days of the current troubles. Overt OPs are a constant terrorist target: note the wire mesh screen protecting against mortar, grenade and rocket attack, and the filled oildrums designed to prevent car bombs being driven into the position.*

*An urban OP like this must be adequately defended, and mutually supported by other posts. Note the sandbagging and the GPMG. The hessian screen allows movement and observation without giving a sniper a clear target. Overt OPs limit terrorist activity by their presence.*

# Combat Skills

observation. A radio with either burst transmission facilities, like the Racal Merod system, or frequency agility, which hops through a range of frequencies, will prevent the enemy getting a fix on your OP when you transmit information.

## Frequency-hopping

The advantage of frequency agility is that you can transmit as events are happening and so correct artillery fire. If you use burst transmission you will have to format the message on the display and then send it. When you are using SOP (Standard Operating Procedure) formatted messages, burst transmission is the ideal system.

**Types of OP**
In conventional war, the work is divided between the infantry, who would set up this sort of OP, and armoured reconnaissance regiments of the Royal Armoured Corps, whose Scorpions and Scimitars would provide mobile OPs.

**Construction**
This type of OP may take several days to construct and uses large quantities of sandbags, angle-iron pickets, wire and wriggly tin (corrugated iron). You may be able to find old doors, or lengths of felled timber (common in German woods) to help with the job. Excavated soil must be disposed of thoughtfully, either spread on tracks or dumped in streams or manpacked some distance away.

**The observer**
His job is to observe his and report any enemy activity. In Germany, OF would be used to disco the direction of the mai thrust of the Soviet Operational Manoeuvre Group seeking to penet NATO's defences.

**NBC protection**
In a future war, OP members will almost certainly need to wear NBC suits, so the use of surveillance equipment must be practised in full NBC kit. If the OP is to be maintained for a number of days, spare suits and gloves will have to be manpacked in.

**Protection**
This four-man OP relies upon concealment for its protection. It is completely dug in, and revetted like a main battle trench, with at least 45cm of overhead cover for protection against shell splinters.

**Kipmat**
This makes life easier as it provides insulation from the cold ground.

**Rest bay**
In a four-man OP party, only two sleeping bags are required as two people are always on duty. They should not be zipped when in use to allow for rapid evacuation. Kit not in use must be packed away at all times. It is unlikely that the tactical situation will allow you to cook, and even if you can you must remember that hexamine smells, and also gives off poisonous fumes which can accumulate dangerously in an enclosed space.

**Immersion suits**
Aircrew immersion suits are very useful in OPs. Alternatively, wear your waterproofs nderneath your combat jacket.

**Kit layout**
Four Bergens never seem be enough to carry the required kit. Bergen weight of more than 40kg are not uncommon. One of the fou packs contains communications equipmen a second carries the food and uncontaminated water The other two are for surveillance devices, specia equipment, spare clothes and sleeping bags. All members of the OP party must be familiar with the contents of all the Bergens in case of emergency or the absence of a patrol membe

Other electronic aids include the simple dictaphone hand-held tape recorder. Instead of writing notes, sometimes in the dark or in bad weather, you can record the events that you are observing. Again remember spare tapes and spare batteries. If you can work with light, make sure that flashlights are as small as possible and have red filters to save your night vision and reduce the danger of enemy observation – again, make sure the batteries are fresh. The Betalight is useful: it has a long life and compact configuration.

Cameras come into their own when you are in a CRW (Counter Revolutionary Warfare) environment.

# A COVERT OBSERVATION POST ON THE CENTRAL FRONT

*In order to make informed decisions, commanders need the maximum possible battlefield intelligence about the enemy's strengths, movements, positions, habits, dress, and possible intentions. In any future European conflict, a very effective way of getting that intelligence is by the use of observation posts.*

Wanted men, suspect vehicles and illegal gatherings can be photographed and checked with intelligence records after the OP is completed and debriefed. Cameras are also useful when you are tasked with enemy vehicle identification.

## High-tech aids

Though a laser rangefinder is useful, it is an active source and may alert the enemy to your location. Laser beams can be detected by sensors on enemy AFVs. Passive night vision equipment, either long-range tripod mounted systems or simply the IWS from a rifle, will give you good short-range observation. If you are an artillery observer the longer range systems

**Sentry**
He shares with the observer the task of using the wide variety of surveillance equipment. He also operates the radio, and is responsible for the protection of the OP. He may also help with the preparation of a detailed sketch map/range card and assist in keeping the OP log.

**Radio**
Use of radio must be kept to a minimum to forestall enemy eavesdropping and direction-finding.

**Clothing**
On the patrol into the OP, you will sweat excessively. Wear a T-shirt under your combat gear to prevent suffering from chilling when you stop moving. The same goes for the work phase when you are setting up the OP: as soon as you stop work and occupy the OP, you must put on several layers of warm, dry clothing. Once inside the confined space, physical movement will be kept to a minimum and you will become much colder than normal; hypothermia may be a problem.

# ROUTINE IN A SIMPLE O.P.

In a basic OP, there are four positions. The observer and the radio operator/observer maintain the watch, swapping roles every 20 minutes or so to prevent tiredness. The third man sleeps or attends to personal tasks while the fourth, armed with an LSW, acts as rear sentry. The members of the party rotate anti-clockwise through the positions at hourly intervals.

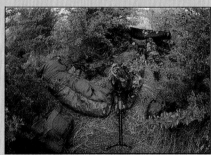

On a given signal, the observer wakes the sleeper and takes the sleeping bag. The sleeper moves onto sentry duty, while the sentry takes over the radio operator/observer's position. The radio operator passes across the headset and moves onto observation. No equipment or weapons are moved in the changeover of personnel.

# THE EYES OF THE ARMY
## Equipped for OP Duty

**1 Gillie suit**
Personal camouflage and concealment must be excellent.
**2 Thermos flask**
**3 Poncho**
**4 Entrenching tool**
**5 Sleeping bag**
Protect it with a Gore-Tex waterproof bivi-bag, because once wet army issue bags are useless.
**6 Bergen**
This needs to be comfortable and of large capacity.
**7 Kipmat**
**8 Claymore mine**
Good for providing close-in protection should your OP be compromised.
**9 M79 grenade launcher**
If you are attacked the grenade launcher may help you turn the tables and win the fire-fight.
**10 M16 (Armalite) assault rifle**
A lightweight weapon ideal for OP work.
**11 Camera equipment and lenses**
**12 Passive night vision goggles**
For use on the route in as well as on the OP.
**13 Scrim net**
**14 Hand-held thermal imager**

*This Royal Marine on a rooftop OP is carrying an Individual Weapon Sight fitted to an SLR. Urban covert OPs are a good deal easier to set up as there is no shortage of suitable derelict housing. Be careful with the IWS; it emits a low whine when switched on which can be heard at 15 metres.*

are clearly necessary, but passive systems with a range of 150 metres will allow you to stake out a position by night.

At the other end of the technology scale are the basic bodily functions: eating and defecating. Food cannot normally be cooked as smells carry long distances, but insulated containers may allow you to take hot food into the field. There are some chemical-based systems such as the US Zesto-Therm, which consists of a small chemical sachet, and insulated bag or pouch. By putting one in the pouch, adding water and placing in a food sachet, you can have warm food. The only drawback there is a slight chemical smell which may compromise the position or may simply be unpleasant to live with.

## Waste disposal
Food and water will have to be carried in, and all waste carried out. Use plastic bin liners for all rubbish: double ones are best, and do not overload them. Remember, you will have to take them out in your Bergens! If you take an anti-diarrhoea tablet when you are in the OP this will induce constipation and get you through the OP patrol, but may be

*Electronics have transformed the art of night surveillance. The hand-held thermal imager seen here is in use with a scan converter, allowing the image to be viewed (and recorded) on a TV monitor. Better still, the observer can view the display at any convenient secure location some distance from the imager.*

*Unlike the IWS, the Thermal Imager (TI) is not obscured by battlefield smoke or fog, and remains effective even on the darkest night.*

rather disruptive to your bowels.

Communications in the OP may be by speech, but it may also be necessary to use cards, carrying messages such as 'Your Stag Now'.

## Last resort
Hopefully you will not have to fight in your OP; if you do, something's gone very wrong. Weapons need to be compact, but capable of a high rate of fire. The Colt 733 Commando assault rifle, with a 30-round magazine, is ideal. Pistols with a silencer will allow you to kill an enemy who may have blundered into the position.

Area mines like the British PAD mine or the US Claymore will give good overall cover against infantry, but may compromise the position when they are emplaced: like unattended ground sensors (UGS), which have to be pre-positioned in a perimeter around the OP, they may be detected by the enemy. UGS, however will give you advanced warning of enemy movement, whether wheeled, tracked or even men on foot. UGS can even be configured to detect speech, seismic tremors and metallic masses such as AFVs.

Finally, good-quality clothing and a first-aid kit and medically-trained team member are essential. The kit should not only contain morphine and first field dressings and pads, but also plasters for minor cuts that might become septic in the OP, and simple pain killers for headaches and stomach troubles.

## Warm clothing

Personal protection will include sleeping bags with a Velcro and zip opening to allow quick exits in the event of an emergency. Quilted clothing and even quilted foot wear may be necessary, since OP work can be cold and there is absolutely no opportunity to move about to improve circulation. Thermal underclothes and thermal boots may also be required, plus gloves as both camouflage and for protection.

Perhaps the most important thing about OP work is being able to get on with your mates. You may have to sleep, eat and defecate in their company, so make friends fast.

A successful OP requires a high standard of camouflage and concealment, effective patrolling techniques, highly efficient administration and preparation, good terrorist or AFV recognition, effective survival techniques – and the patience of Job. If you can master all this you are a professional.

*Above and right: British troops at an observation post in Belize may be experiencing a climate very different from that of South Armagh, but the watch on the Guatemalan border requires patience and concentration just as much as in an OP in Ulster's bandit country. Inside the post, the spotting scopes are prominent. Note the large photograph with the OP's arcs of observation and ranges marked on.*

# ALTERNATIVE OP LAYOUTS

## Star formation

Layout depends on the size, location and the nature of the cover in which the OP is located. When digging the OP, be careful not to spill loose earth around the position, and keep the turves used on the overhead cover in good condition: you may even need to water them. The star formation is generally considered the best.

**1** Sentry
**2** Observation position
**3** Rest bay
**4** Rest bay (personal admin)
**5** Central well holding spare kit

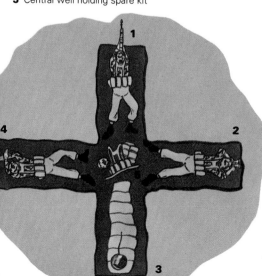

## Pairs

The pairs layout is good for putting into linear features such as fencelines and boundaries. Observation ports should be kept small, with a face veil or camouflage net draped over the opening. The observation bay is screened from any light source within the OP by a black hessian screen

**1** Rest bay and personal admin
**2** Kit well
**3** Observer and sentry

## Top to tail

This layout is largely intended for use underneath or within bushes. Again, it is good for use along linear features and it is suitable for all-round observation.

**1** Sentry
**2** Rest bay (personal admin)
**3** Rest bay
**4** Observer

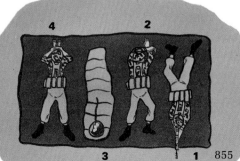

# Combat Report
## Kenya:
## Disarming the Turkana Tribesmen

Captured rifles taken from the Turkana tribesmen. The operation greatly reduced the tribal arsenal but did not prevent further armed border raids.

**Early in 1962 in Turkana, Kenya, the 5th Battalion of the King's African Rifles, assisted by the Kenya Police and the British Army Air Corps, carried out an extensive operation to try to disarm the Turkana tribesmen.**

Turkana lies in northern Kenya and borders on Uganda, Sudan and Ethiopia. It is a wild, inhospitable place of desert, scrub and lava rock. There is little or no water, and in 1962 there were no proper roads, just rough tracks which were barely motorable.

The battalion started its journey northwards from our base at Nakuru in the Rift Valley, staying the night at a place called Kakuma. By the size of the map's lettering, we assumed this to be a small township or village. In fact, it turned out to be a crossing place on a dried-up river bed, which was marked by a human skull. The place planned for Battalion Tactical Headquarters was also prominently marked. Called Lokochogio, it consisted of one empty tin shack!

### Eight cows per weapon

The Turkana are a tough, proud and nomadic people, and they and the Karamajong of Uganda have always raided each other. However, the use of newly acquired Steyr rifles had escalated the casualties on both sides. These old Austrian rifles cost eight cows per weapon, so each time the Turkana stole cattle they increased their armoury. In under two years, 174 Ugandan tribesmen and 117 Turkana had been killed, so the authorities had decided to mount a disarming operation, called 'Operation Utah'.

For this operation troops were also invited from Uganda, which, at the time, was under the command of Idi Amin, and as the Ugandans had

**A British Army Air Corps Alouette II takes off from a Kenyan landing zone. These French helicopters were widely used in the early 1960s.**

always regarded the Turkana as worse than animals the results were predictable.

We, the 5th King's African Rifles, moved into this rugged, desolate area and set up base camps from which we patrolled, while air reconnaissance informed us of the Turkana's whereabouts. When groups were found they were rounded up and taken to specific areas where water and grazing were available. The women, children and old men were allowed to go free, but the young men were held in captivity. Being separated from their beloved cattle and imprisoned was a constant source of irritation to these men.

It was then explained to them that if they were prepared to go and collect a hidden rifle and surrender it, they could go free. Some agreed straight away, but most just sat in the blazing sun and glared at us. Those who had agreed would disappear for several days and eventually return with their precious rifles. Our pile of illegal arms slowly grew.

Sometimes the Turkana fought back, and on one occasion they threw spears at one of our patrols. The patrol opened fire, shooting two warriors, whose bodies were buried in a dried-up river bed near Battalion HQ. The soldiers dug an especially deep grave because of the hyenas and other animals, and then covered it with large rocks and 'bide-a-while' thorn, which has awesome one-inch spines.

### The laughter of hyenas

That night I was woken up in my scorchingly hot tent by a weird, unusual clamour. All my senses called 'Danger', and I was ready to reach for my rifle. Then I realised what the sounds were: the eerie laughing of hyenas, plus the gruesome noise of human bones being crunched in powerful jaws. So much for the deep, boulder-covered grave, I thought, and tried to return to my sweaty sleep.

The following morning we went to the spot, where to our amazement we found that the

hyenas hadn't bothered to move the rocks or thorn bushes. Instead they had dug a neat tunnel about four metres long. All that was left was one piece of human skull and fragments of torn Army blankets.

After nearly two months, 'Operation Utah' drew to a close. In total, 183 rifles and 540 rounds of ammunition had been collected.

As we began to return to our bases, an enormous row broke out over allegations that Idi Amin's company had tortured 13 prisoners to death. As Uganda was independent, the matter was never resolved.

So, hot, tired and scruffy, with most of our vehicles in sore need of repair, we slowly returned to our comfortable barracks. Everyone felt that our efforts had helped to preserve peace in the area. However, five days later came a police report saying that 200 Turkana tribesmen, heavily armed, mainly with rifles, had carried out a raid into Uganda, killing many people and stealing several hundred head of cattle.

# SETTING UP ROADBLOCKS

*Roadblocks are usually mounted in an internal security (IS) or counter-insurgency situation. You can use either snap or permanent roadblocks; the purpose of both is to check traffic going through a particular point or to completely block a road to prevent its further use.* The siting of the roadblock is important. Preferably, it should be around a corner or beyond the crest of a hill so as to take the driver by surprise, and should be flanked by hedgerows or ditches so that it is difficult or impossible for a car to turn round.

Terrorists have to use wheeled transport to move weapons, explosives, supplies and other equipment to safe hiding-places, from which they will have to move them again when they intend to use them. The best way to counter this threat is to create a permanent infrastructure of roadblocks, or vehicle checkpoints (VCPs) as they are called in Northern Ireland, upon which you can superimpose as many extra snap or temporary roadblocks or VCPs as the operational situation demands.

## Permanent roadblocks

The basic, permanent VCP will impose restrictions on the terrorist. Even though he knows it is there and the surprise element is lacking, it forces him to use other routes, thereby reducing his options; it also reduces the number of routes upon which you need mount snap or temporary VCPs. Snap VCPs can be set up by foot patrols, by vehicle patrols or by patrols dropped from a helicopter. This latter technique is known by the British Army in Northern Ireland as an Eagle Patrol.

*Freedom fighters or terrorists use similar tactics to the security forces. Here an El Salvadorean guerrilla demonstrates his control of this section of the coastal highway only 50 km from the capital. Burning trucks provide an adequate road block.*

## THE AIMS OF ROADBLOCKS AND VCPs

**They should:**

1. **Dominate the area, deterring terrorist activity and movement.**
2. **Prevent reinforcements of enemy or terrorists reaching sensitive areas or riotous gatherings.**
3. **Deny contact between terrorists and local inhabitants.**
4. **Prevent supply of arms, ammo, food and medical supplies to the enemy.**
5. **Win public confidence and impress the local inhabitants.**
6. **Facilitate other operations against the enemy or terrorists.**
7. **Gain information and intelligence.**

# Combat Skills

## LAYOUT OF A VCP

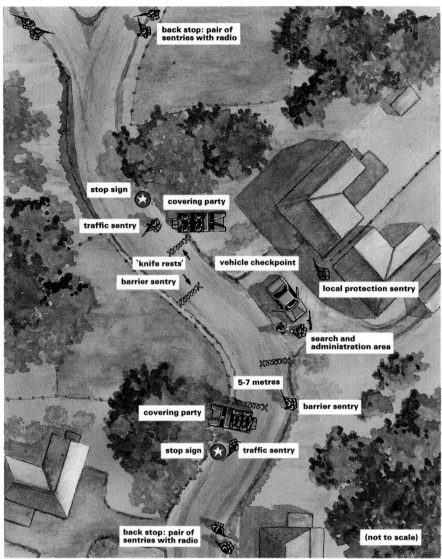

A VCP can be set up simply by putting two parallel lines of knife rests (barbed wire frames) about 50 metres apart on the road; you can do the same with vehicles. The enclosure formed can be used as a search area. The number of troops you'll need for the job depends on how many roads you are covering and how busy they are. If possible, all road blocks should be co-ordinated and manned by civilian police along with the military personnel.

**Above: A Royal Marine Commando lifts an anti-tank mine laid by Argentine forces on the verge of one of the roads approaching Port Stanley. Permanent roadblocks can remain effective long after the end of the battle.**

Permanent roadblocks or VCPs must be well defended, permanently manned and well equipped. The smallest practical unit that can look after itself is a section: this is just big enough to run a shift system 24 hours a day. The position should provide safe accommodation for those not on duty and reliable communications to your HQ. Your perimeter should be well defended with wire to prevent attack or fire, and with concrete bollards to prevent terrorists leaving a car bomb alongside your position.

Surveillance aids such as remotely-controlled CCTV cameras can monitor approaches that you may not be able to see all the time. Your roadblock will probably be sited on a busy road or border crossing, and your job will be to check the identity of all those passing through your position and also to search them. Your aim is to limit the movement of both terrorists and their weapons and explosives.

### Proper planning

Clearly, if the road is very busy you will not have sufficient men to search all vehicles without causing a major traffic jam. Either you will have to select vehicles at random for checking, or you will need additional police or military manpower. If you intend to bodysearch females you will need female soldiers or policewomen. If your roadblock is to be effective at night, floodlights will be necessary.

A permanent roadblock is vulnerable to attack and therefore it must take on all the characteristics of a military base. It will tend to suck up more and more manpower, and you must use all your ingenuity to use as few men as possible by employing mechanical items such as 'sleeping policemen', chicanes, surveillance devices, secure and strong defences, good communications and so on.

### Snap roadblocks

When you mount a snap roadblock you are under fewer constraints: because you will be in position only for a short period, the enemy is unlikely to have the time to organise and mount an attack upon you, unless you compromise him in a roadblock and he tries to evade it or crash through it.

Snap roadblocks can be mounted by section-strength foot or vehicle patrols whenever and wherever the moment is right. The technique is to half-block the road with your vehicle and, if you have two vehicles, to create a chicane effect by blocking alternate sides of the road at an interval of per-

*In conventional warfare, roadblocks are designed to slow down or channel an enemy's advance. Mining adds to the effectiveness, as shown by this Israeli soldier prodding gently for mines.*

haps 25 metres. This will force traffic to slow down to be checked.

If you are on foot or have been dropped from a helicopter, you won't have any vehicles to help you. You may have a portable Caltrop (an extendable arm with upward-pointing spikes designed to cause punctures to car tyres), but this is normally used in an emergency to stop an escaping vehicle. Often you will have to rely on vehicles heeding your signal to stop. Law-abiding citizens will of course do this.

## Stopping and checking

At least two members of your patrol will need to carry out the job of stopping and checking passing vehicles, and at least another two men should be employed to cover the checkers. These men should be far enough back so as not to get in the searchers' way, but close enough to be able to see what is going on.

## A BAD NIGHT IN BELFAST

*A car that had burst through an army/ RUC vehicle checkpoint was pursued by a chase vehicle to this rather unfortunate end; it crashed during the high-speed chase. The Army's job in the province is complicated by drunken joyriders and car thieves, who could just as easily be heavily-armed terrorists. You cannot open fire just because a vehicle fails to stop.*

# Combat Skills

Precise orders for opening fire will have been given. In an IS situation, this usually means that you can only open fire if your own or one of your comrades' lives, or that of another innocent person, is threatened. You must be absolutely sure that you understand your orders: a car simply failing to stop at a roadblock is not normally sufficient reason to open fire.

*Argyll and Sutherland Highlanders search a suspect's car at a roadblock in Aden. Note that the searcher is covered at all times by his number two.*

As well as the men employed in stopping and checking the traffic and those covering them, you will need to position 'long stops' in both directions down the road. Their task is to cut off anyone who approaches the roadblock, sees it, thinks better of going through it and turns round to go back the other way. Alternatively, they can attempt to stop someone who has

crashed the roadblock, short of opening fire, which will not usually be possible unless the occupants of the car have opened fire at you.

## Escaping cars

There are not too many options open to you for halting a car that is quite determined not to stop. Caltrop can be very effective if you can deploy it in time, and armoured vehicles are even more effective if you are part of a vehicle patrol. However, if you are unable to stop an escaping car you should either have a pursuit vehicle ready to give chase or be in radio contact with a police or military vehicle that can give chase. At the very least

**Traffic control**
If traffic volume is heavy, members of the checkpoint must bear in mind basic road safety and prevention of accidents.

**Layout**
Stop groups should be on each side and well clear of the search area so that they can watch approaching traffic, prevent vehicles or people evading the VCP and watch out for snipers or other enemy forces moving into position. It should not be possible to drive round the VCP, so it must be sited with ditches or obstacles on each side of the road. Vehicles placed in an arrowhead formation will make it impossible to drive through at speed, while permitting a slow through-flow of traffic.

**Communications**
A VCP must have excellent communications so that information about suspect vehicles or individuals such as number plate or identity checks can be rapidly obtained. Revised instructions or orders must be passed swiftly from HQ, as well as immediate reaction from stop groups or hot pursuit vehicles.

you will have a description of the car and a registration number, which should make its subsequent apprehension quite easy.

Roadblocks are relatively simple to mount. Remember these basic rules, and you can successfully apprehend wanted men or uncover a haul of illegal arms or explosives.

**Early warning devices**
Unmanned ground sensors such as Classic can be set to detect vehicles or personnel approaching the VCP from up to several kilometres away. Ground radar and infra-red devices can also be used.

**Security**
A VCP must have enough men to defend itself from enemy ambush, especially when moving in and setting up. It should be treated just like a patrol. Remember, a security force VCP is a high-value terrorist target.

**Concealment**
A good VCP should be sited where it is difficult for a terrorist to turn his vehicle round or reverse out without being noticed by the VCP. Sharp bends or dips in the road are the places to go for.

# A VEHICLE CHECKPOINT

*Vehicle Checkpoints (VCPs) are set up during emergencies both to apprehend wanted persons and to prevent the smuggling of arms and equipment. Checkpoints also enhance the visibility of the forces of law and order, acting as a deterrent.*

*Below: The ultimate roadblock. There is no squeezing your car-bomb past this in a hurry! A T-54 of the Shi'ite Amal militia guards the approaches to the Beirut residence of the Amal leader, Nabit Berri. Tanks are effective, moveable roadblocks with massive firepower: even when knocked out by terrorists, they are still 40 or 50 tonnes of metal blocking the middle of the road.*

**Automatic fire**
Machine-gun fire can be called for by the commander on the spot in the same way that he requests single shots, if in his judgement it is the minimum force required and that no other weapon can be used effectively. Short bursts minimise risks to bystanders.

**Stop groups**
These are more effective if they are concealed. If you have time, dig in. Make sure communications between the stop groups and the search area are duplicated (e.g. both radio and field telephone). The stop groups should have weapons capable of stopping a car, and pre-designated arcs of fire and killing zones. A quick and effective way of blocking the road should be available, such as vehicles or Caltrops, shown here.

**Moving out**
Before leaving the position, make a detailed search along the sides of the road in both directions to the limit of visibility. You may find some things that people with guilty consciences dumped out of car windows while approaching the VCP.

# CONTROLLING BLEEDING

**When you've got the casualty breathing again, you can turn your attention to controlling any bleeding: the second most common cause of death from injury.** Bleeding may be in the form of a slow ooze from the very smallest of blood vessels, or a much more rapid loss from a major vessel. If it's spurting out, it is coming from an artery, and this is very serious.

Occasionally, bleeding stops of its own accord, either from retraction of the blood vessels or clotting of the blood, but this is likely only with small or superficial wounds.

## First steps

These simple measures will help to control bleeding in most cases. Points 2 and 4 apply to injured limbs.

### 1 Place the casualty in a comfortable position
This reduces the blood flow, as his heart will be making less effort to pump blood.

### 2 Raise the limb
This also reduces bleeding, but think carefully before doing this in case you cause further injury. If in doubt, don't.

*Below: Control the bleeding straight away with direct pressure on the wound. Use a piece of cloth, a cap, face veil, beret or even your hand. Elevate the injured part if you can, because this will reduce the flow. Keep the pressure on while you open the shell dressing, and try not to touch the inside of the dressing.*

*Above: The most important factor in dealing with bleeding is speed! But make sure that you are treating the most serious wound. Check over the whole body and, in the case of gunshot wounds, do not expect the exit hole to be in line with the entry point.*

*The dressing has 'other side to wound' written on one side. The pad must cover the whole wound and must be tight, or you will waste time and blood. The brown bandage is attached to the pad and, if the casualty is conscious, he can hold it in place while you bandage. Make sure all the pad is covered by the brown bandage.*

### 3 Apply pressure to the bleeding wound

This will often stop the bleeding completely: place a dressing over the wound and apply pressure with the palm of your hand. Make sure the dressing is big enough, and use a sterile one if available; but any piece of clean material will do. If you can't find a dressing big enough to cover the wound, press it down where the bleeding is worst. If bleeding continues despite pressure, apply a second dressing on top of the first. Do not lift the first one to see what is happening! You can apply up to three dressings, and none should be removed until the casualty gets to hospital.

### 4 Immobilise the limb

*Below: Brachial Pressure Point*
*By pressing firmly in the armpit with your thumb you squash the artery against the bone and reduce the flow of blood to a wound on the arm.*

*Above: If the blood comes through the dressing, strap another one on top. Do not remove the original. If you get past three dressings, you will need to use a pressure point. Once the bleeding is controlled, immobilise the limb and remember not to use a white triangular bandage in a tactical situation!*

## Pressure points

Any place where an artery crosses a bone close to the skin is a pressure point; pressure applied at these areas will, in theory, interrupt the blood flow. If the pressure point is between the heart and the bleeding point, you may be able to stop the flow altogether.

In practice, only two pressure points are of much use: the Brachial and Femoral areas. Direct, firm pressure at these points can be used to stop bleeding in the arms and legs. To carry out the procedure:
1 Place the thumb or fingers over the pressure point.
2 Apply sufficient pressure to stop the blood flow and hence the bleeding.
3 After 15 minutes, slowly release the pressure.
4 If bleeding has stopped, dress the wound.
5 If bleeding starts again, repeat the process.

The release of pressure after 15 minutes is essential to allow blood to reach the tissues beyond the pressure point; if this is not done, they may be damaged. Resist the temptation to release pressure in under 15 minutes to see how you are getting on, as bleeding will not yet have been controlled.

## Internal bleeding

Internal bleeding is harder to deal with. It may have been caused by a severe blow to the abdomen, a crush injury to the chest, or by the blast effects of an explosion. Also, if a bone is broken, especially a large one such as the femur (thigh bone), there will be bleeding in the surrounding tissue. Internal bleeding can cause any or all of the following symptoms:

1 Pallor
2 Cold, clammy skin
3 Rapid, weak pulse
4 Restlessness and weakness

Treatment is difficult and depends on rapid evacuation to hospital. In the meantime, talk to the casualty and make him as warm and comfortable as you can.

*Below: Femoral Pressure Point*
*Firm pressure inside the groin will press the femoral arteries against the pelvic basin and reduce blood flow to a wound on the legs.*

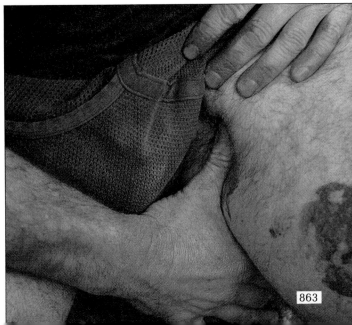

# DEALING WITH FRACTURES

***When you've dealt with the casualty's breathing and bleeding, the third priority is broken bones.*** Fractured bones can cause serious injury or death, but can often be successfully treated and a complete recovery achieved. A great deal depends on the first aid you give the casualty before he is evacuated for treatment. Before he can be moved you must immobilise the fracture: the basic principle of splinting is to immobilise the joints above and below the break.

## Immobilising fractures

You must keep the fracture still to prevent the sharp edges of the broken bone moving about. This achieves three things:

**1** Stops further damage to tissue, muscle, blood vessels and nerves
**2** Reduces pain and shock
**3** Stops a closed fracture becoming an open one because of bone fragments penetrating the skin.

## Rules for splinting

**1** Remove watches, rings and garments from the limb, or these may reduce the flow of blood to the hand or foot when the injured part becomes swollen.
**2** If the tactical situation allows it, splint the fractured part before moving the casualty and without any change in the position of the fractured part. If a bone is in an unnatural position or a joint is bent, leave it as it is.

If circumstances force you to move a casualty with fractures in his lower body before you can apply a splint, tie the injured leg to his other leg. Grasp the casualty beneath his armpits and pull him in a straight line. Do not roll or move him sideways.
**3** Apply the splint so that the joint above the fracture and the joint below the fracture are completely immobilised.
**4** Place some padding between the splint and the injured area. This is especially important between the legs, in the armpits and in areas where the splint rests against bony parts such as the wrist, knee or ankle joint.
**5** Bind the splint with bandages in several places above and below the fracture, but not so tightly that it interferes with the flow of blood. Do not bandage across the fracture. Tie bandages with a non-slip knot against the splint.

*Above and below: You can immobilise a casualty's leg by securing it to his other leg with (top to bottom) his face veil, webbing, and SLR sling. If you must move him, do so in a straight line lengthwise; do not roll him or push him sideways.*

# Signs and symptoms

Symptoms of a fracture include pain when slight pressure is applied to the injured area, and sharp pain when the casualty tried to move the area. Do not move him or encourage him to move in order to identify a fracture, because the movement could cause further damage and lead to shock. Other signs are swelling, unnatural movement of the limb, bruising, and crepitus (the distinctive sound of fractured bone ends grating together).

# Types of fracture

**1 Open fracture**
An open fracture is a break in the bone and in the overlying skin and flesh. The broken bone may have punctured the skin, or a bullet may have penetrated the skin and broken the bone.

**2 Closed fracture**
In a closed fracture, the bone is broken but the skin remains intact. There may be tissue damage, and the area is likely to swell and later bruise. It may only be a sprain, but you should assume the worse and treat it like a fracture.

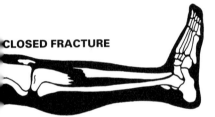

**CLOSED FRACTURE**

**bone not protruding (usually no bleeding)**

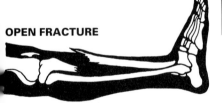

**OPEN FRACTURE**

**bone protruding (usually bleeding)**

**OPEN FRACTURE PRODUCED BY MISSILE**

**open (usually bleeding)**

*If you have nothing with which to construct a splint, immobilise an injured arm by securing it to the casualty's chest. Slings can be improvised from belts or bits of shirts or blankets. Remember to put some padding between the splint and the injured arm.*

# Slings

Use a sling to support the following:

**1** A splinted arm bent at the elbow
**2** A sprained arm
**3** An arm with a painful wound

*Slip the triangular bandage underneath the injured arm.*

*Fold it up and tie it behind the casualty's neck. Secure the elbow edge with a safety pin if possible.*

*An elevation sling, used to help control bleeding, is made differently: gently fold the lower edge of the triangular bandage under the injured arm.*

*Bring it round the casualty's back and the front of the uninjured shoulder. Tie the ends together with a reef knot.*

# Improvised slings

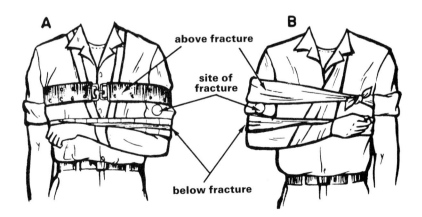

above fracture

site of fracture

below fracture

**BELT, PISTOL BELT AND BANDOLIER**

**STRIPS FROM CLOTHING OR BLANKET**

# FIRST AID IMPROVISATION

*ARVNs street fighting in Cholon carry one of their section, wounded in the neck and chest: the firefight continues on the other side of the building. When carried like this the casualty is not going to arrive in good condition.*

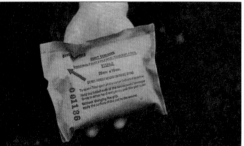

*This is the issue shell dressing, with instructions in English and French.*

*The packet contains the dressing and two safety pins. Open the dressing and apply, gripping the outside edges so that you do not contaminate the inside of the pad.*

***There might come a time when your oppo has been hit and you haven't got the kit to help him.*** But most 'official' first-aid kit is unnecessary, so you should not be tempted to burden yourself with a vast collection of equipment. Every soldier is trained in first aid. The only pieces of equipment he carries are dressings: everything else has got to be improvised.

## Dressings

A field dressing is a large pad of gauze with a bandage attached; ideally it should be in a sterile packet, and each soldier should carry at least three. A lot of dressings that are commercially available are frankly too small: a dressing cannot be too large.

If you cannot find a proper dressing the next best thing is a suitable gauze pad held in place with a crepe bandage. Failing this, any clean material will do: clean cotton is best, so use handkerchiefs or shirts folded to make a pad or torn into strips to make a bandage. If you can't find anything very clean, use the cleanest part up against the wound and the less clean further away. Remember, most gunshot wounds are highly contaminated anyway by the bullet: bits of cloth have been pushed into the wound and dirt sucked in as the temporary cavity caused by the wound repressurises.

*A simulated broken leg is splinted using a section of window frame torn from a building. The new issue stretcher is a collapsible model, lighter and easier to carry than the old World War II type.*

## LEG SPLINTS

*How to apply improvised splints for a fracture of the lower limb or ankle. Note that the knots are against the splints, not the leg.*

# ARM SPLINTS

The aim of splinting is to immobilise the limb and prevent the break getting any worse. Both diagrams show methods of splinting a broken arm or elbow where the elbow is not bent. Try to pad the splint so that the casualty feels comfortable and immobilise the whole arrangement by strapping it down to the chest.

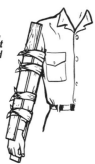

The binding or cravats should be firm enough to prevent movement, but not so tight that they limit the blood flow. Use a wide piece of cloth or bandage so that it does not cut in. Remember to immobilise the joint above and below the fracture.

# Splints

Splints can be made from anything that is reasonably rigid, wooden planks, branches or metal sheeting. Items of military equipment might be suitable, but if you decide to use your rifle pay attention to the tactical situation first. Inflatable splints are carried by the combat medic.

You will need bandages to secure the splint to the body. Almost anything will do, ranging from scarves through other pieces of clothing to belts and various parts of military webbing.

# Stretchers

If you need to evacuate a casualty you will need a stretcher. Lightweight rope stretchers, as used in climbing, are ideal and can be carried one per section. The new issue stretcher is collapsible and can be easily carried in a Bergen.

If you have to improvise, things such as doors and planks are obvious choices, but you may have to make do with branches or rifles. Obviously whatever you use must be as comfortable as possible for the patient. Remember that it must also be reasonably comfortable for those who have to carry it: this becomes increasingly important the further the stretcher has to be carried.

# Carrying

If you do not have a stretcher and haven't time to improvise, you may have to carry the casualty in, for instance, a fireman's lift. There are several ways of making things easier for yourself, particularly in getting the casualty up on to your shoulder.

# ANATOMICAL SPLINT

You can use the uninjured leg as a splint for the fracture: pad out the gaps between the legs before you start tying them together. Leave the boots on and tie them together firmly at the base and the top of the boot. There should be no shortage of things to use as strapping: the picture shows just a few ideas. They must be placed as shown, and this is the minimum number that will be effective.

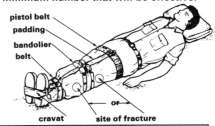

pistol belt
padding
bandolier belt

or

cravat     site of fracture

# THE FIREMAN'S LIFT

The fireman's lift is a good carry position. The only real problem is that if you are on your own and the casualty is unconscious or can't stand, manoeuvring him onto your shoulders is a fairly complicated piece of ballet.

From the recovery position, haul the casualty up onto your knee and balance him there while you change grip to under his armpits. Then heave him onto his feet, leaning against you.

Hold out the casualty's right arm, and then duck under the arm. Put your head against his chest and your left arm between his legs, holding the right knee in the crook of your elbow, and swing him up onto your shoulders. The higher up you carry him, the easier it is. Hold his right arm and leg together in your left hand and carry your rifle in your right hand.

# Su-25 'Frogfoot': Battlefield Blaster

***There is a strong tendency to dismiss Soviet combat aircraft as being markedly inferior to their Western counterparts, sometimes possessing great strength or ruggedness but never being as combat-effective as a Western equivalent.*** As the Soviet Union rapidly closes the technology gap on all fronts, this dangerously complacent attitude becomes further and further from the truth. The Sukhoi Su-25, dubbed 'Frogfoot' by the NATO Air Standards Co-ordinating Committee, is a prime example of this.

## Huge production

While it is indisputably true that the 'Frogfoot' lacks the incredible manoeuvrability, heavy armour and hard-hitting cannon of the Fairchild A-10A Thunderbolt II, its closest equivalent in the West, this does not necessarily make it an inferior or less useful weapon. Indeed, while the

USAF is withdrawing its A-10s because their slow speed makes them vulnerable, the 'Frogfoot' is pouring off the production lines in huge numbers.

During 1967 the USAF issued a specification for a new battlefield anti-tank aircraft, and this resulted in two flying prototypes, the Northrop YA-9A and the Fairchild YA-10A. Both aircraft were designed around a brand new gun of devastating power, firing projectiles that could penetrate even the thickest tank armour.

They were designed for operation from short, semi-prepared airstrips, carrying a heavy load of air-to-surface ordnance for the close air support role. Both aircraft were very simple, lacking any sophisticated avionics equipment, and both were rather slow, although they were highly manoeuvrable.

There is no doubt that the Soviet Union studied the American aircraft

closely, assessing whether a similar aircraft type might be a useful addition to the inventory. During the late 1970s the result of these deliberations became known when US satellites spotted a new aircraft type, resembling the Northrop YA-9A, at the Ramenskoye test airfield outside Moscow.

## Losing US contender

Some Eastern 'experts' have pointed out the irony of the fact that the Soviets based their new aircraft on the losing contender of the USAF competition, but it should be realised that the Fairchild design was selected more on cost and political grounds than for operational reasons.

In any case the new Soviet aircraft, initially code-named 'Ram-J', was not merely a slavish copy of the Northrop aircraft, being lighter and more compact than either American aircraft, and considerably less heavily

*The 'Frogfoot' has a unique and distinctive appearance, quite unlike any other aircraft likely to be encountered over the battlefield.*

armoured. The Soviet aircraft was powered by high-thrust turbojet engines rather than fuel-efficient turbofans, and the wing had a thin high-speed aerofoil section.

The designers clearly placed more emphasis on avoiding ground fire than on being able to simply absorb it. Development of the aircraft was not initially accorded a high priority, and extensive use was made of existing hardware, probably including the navigation and attack avionics of the Su-17 'Fitter', the Tumanskii R-13-300 engine of the MiG-21MF 'Fishbed', the laser ranger and marked target seeker of the MiG-27 'Flogger' and an existing gun – either the standard GSh-23 twin barrel 23-mm cannon or the 30-mm gun carried by the Su-24 'Fencer' and MiG-27 'Flogger'.

### Reporting name assigned

By 1981 it was known that the aircraft was a product of the Sukhoi design bureau, with the Soviet air force designation Su-25, and it was assigned the reporting name 'Frogfoot' during 1982. The aircraft was not ordered into mass production until it had completed a comprehensive evaluation, some of it conducted under operational conditions in Afghanistan during 1981 and 1982 by the 200th Independent Guards Attack Squadron, based at Bagram, near Kabul.

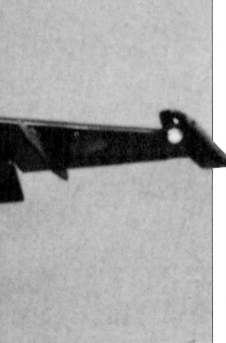

*Above: 'Frogfoot' in take-off configuration. This agile tank-buster carries its 4,500-kg ordnance load on eight underwing pylons, with self-defence air-to-air missiles on two smaller pylons.*

*The 'Frogfoot' pilot can call on sophisticated onboard ECM systems to counter the increasingly effective ground-to-air threat. He sits in an armoured titanium 'bathtub'.*

## 'Frogfoot' anti-tank mission

NATO armour and anti-tank helicopters are slowing down a Warsaw Pact assault, inflicting heavy losses on the attacking Warpac armoured forces. The 'Frogfoot' is used, in conjunction with Mi-24 'Hind' helicopters, to support the advance.

**1** The 'Frogfoot' can operate from semi-prepared grass strips or from conventional airfields, and requires the minimum of servicing support. The aircraft can be quickly re-armed and refuelled, by a small team of men.

**2** 'Frogfoot' would transit to its targets at low altitude, using its superb manoeuvrability to fly Nap-of-Earth.

**3** The Su-25, with its heavy firepower, long range and endurance, is an ideal complement to the Mi-24 'Hind', and co-ordinated tactics have been developed and refined under combat conditions in Afghanistan.

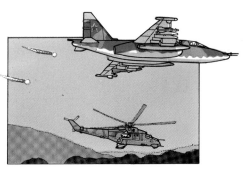

Since then the 'Frogfoot' has seen extensive service in Afghanistan, and has featured heavily in Western television news reports. In Afghanistan the aircraft have usually been seen operating in pairs, with one aircraft attacking a target with gun, bombs or rockets, while the second aircraft flies higher, drawing any hostile fire and ejecting chaff and IR decoy flares, while also pinpointing the location of enemy guns.

## Afghanistan weapons

Weapons used against the Afghan guerrillas have included various types of unguided rocket, with high explosive and incendiary warheads, general-purpose HE bombs, some retarded, some slick, and possibly including laser-guided weapons, and a wide range of specialised anti-personnel weapons.

The latter range from simple cluster bombs with delayed action bomblets, or bomblets disguised as toys, various mines and chemical and incendiary weapons. Chemical agents used in Afghanistan have included both persistent and non-persistent weapons, with nerve gases, choking and blistering gases and substances which attack the blood.

## Short-term effect

Non-lethal incapacitants which cause short-term unconsciousness may also have been used. Self-igniting incendiaries have been dropped by the 'Frogfoot', as have previously unknown stores which distribute an adhesive liquid that bursts into flames when trodden on or driven over.

The aircraft has also delivered various types of fuel/air explosive weapon, which kill by fire or burning off the oxygen in the air, causing huge

# Inside the 'Frogfoot'

An Su-25 of the Czech air force in typical ground attack configuration. The rocket pods shown are of a hitherto unknown type, possibly of local design, but conventional UV-57 series pods can also be carried. Retarded BETA-B bombs and AA-8 'Aphid' air-to-air missiles are also shown here.

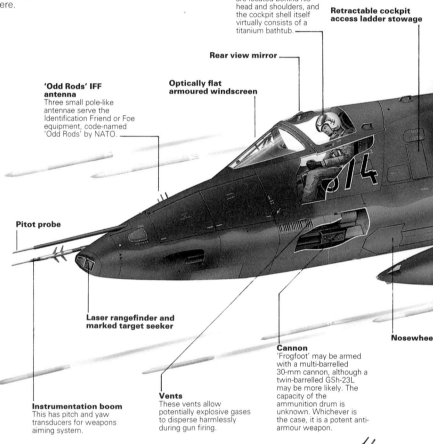

**Pilot**
The pilot sits on a KM-1 series zero-zero ejection seat, in a well-armoured cockpit. Titanium shields are located behind his head and shoulders, and the cockpit shell itself virtually consists of a titanium bathtub.

**Retractable cockpit access ladder stowage**

**Rear view mirror**

**Optically flat armoured windscreen**

**'Odd Rods' IFF antenna**
Three small pole-like antennae serve the Identification Friend or Foe equipment, code-named 'Odd Rods' by NATO.

**Pitot probe**

**Laser rangefinder and marked target seeker**

**Instrumentation boom**
This has pitch and yaw transducers for weapons aiming system.

**Vents**
These vents allow potentially explosive gases to disperse harmlessly during gun firing.

**Cannon**
'Frogfoot' may be armed with a multi-barrelled 30-mm cannon, although a twin-barrelled GSh-23L may be more likely. The capacity of the ammunition drum is unknown. Whichever is the case, it is a potent anti-armour weapon.

**Nosewheel**

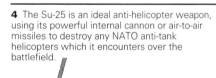

**4** The Su-25 is an ideal anti-helicopter weapon, using its powerful internal cannon or air-to-air missiles to destroy any NATO anti-tank helicopters which it encounters over the battlefield.

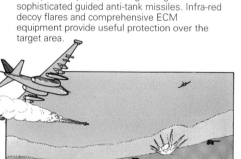

**5 Below:** The 'Frogfoot' can be armed with a variety of weapons, including a range of sophisticated guided anti-tank missiles. Infra-red decoy flares and comprehensive ECM equipment provide useful protection over the target area.

**6 Right:** Cluster bombs, with various types of sub-munition, are extremely effective against soft or lightly armoured targets. The 'Frogfoot' can carry a heavy load of such weapons, and deliver them with unerring accuracy.

**UHF aerial fairing**

**Hydraulically powered twin-segment rudder**

**Rocket pods**
Czech Su-25s have been noted carrying unusual 20-shot rocket pods, probably of indigenous design and manufacture. The size of the rocket projectiles fired is unknown. The pods closely resemble the French Matra SNEB pods in size and appearance. Other operators use the standard UV-32-57 pod.

**BETA-B new pattern 250-kg retarded bomb**

**AA-8 'Aphid' infra red homing air-to-air missile**

**VHF communications aerial**

**Brake parachute housing and chaff/ flare dispenser**

**HF aerial**

**Cooling ram air intake**

**600-litre auxiliary fuel tank**
Jettisonable fuel tanks can be carried on the inboard or centre pylons. The use of such tanks considerably extends the range of the Su-25.

**Main landing gear bays**

**Wingtip fairings**
The wingtip fairings incorporate forward-facing radar warning receiver antennae, retractable landing lamps, navigation lights, and split trailing edge airbrakes. The large blade aerials signify a new updated ECM fit.

over-pressure. The devastatingly effective 500-kg ZAB-5-incendiary bomb is thought to have been used operationally.

The 'Frogfoot' has frequently been used to support attacks by Mil Mi-24 'Hind' and Mi-8 'Hip' helicopter gunships. The 'Frogfoot' can act as an escort, and is able to loiter for longer in the target area. It is less vulnerable to ground fire and is therefore used for fire suppression, using its agility to avoid ground fire and its heavy weapon load to deliver a knockout blow.

The recent introduction of Blowpipe and Stinger shoulder-launched surface-to-air missiles has forced the 'Frogfoot' pilots to develop new tactics, and to make use of new infra-red decoy flares. Tactics developed in Afghanistan are often directly applicable in Central Europe, and it is believed that the rapid rotation of pilots through Afghanistan is giving a huge number of 'Frogfoot' pilots real combat experience.

The upgrading of Soviet tactical air power is currently enjoying a high priority, and the combat-proven Su-25 has benefitted from this trend. From being a type serving only in small numbers for little more than trials use, the 'Frogfoot' has become a major combat type, and is now being produced in sufficient numbers to equip Soviet and Warsaw Pact air

**7 Left:** Unwary NATO fighters and close support aircraft can all fall prey to 'Frogfoot', with its built-in cannon and self defence air-to-air missiles. Any fighter pilot attacking a formation of Su-25s must look behind him frequently.

**9 Below:** The 'Frogfoot' is pulled up to a halt using large twin braking parachutes, then taxis quickly to its dispersal to be rearmed and refuelled for another sortie against NATO armour.

**8 Above:** The Su-25 employs an array of high-lift devices, including trailing edge flaps, leading edge slats, and powerful wingtip airbrakes, to allow it to operate from short runways.

forces, and even to be exported to Iraq for use in the Gulf War against Iran.

The Su-25 is ideally suited to the close air support role in Europe, able to use its manoeuvrability, terrain masking and a sophisticated on-board defensive avionics suite to outwit and avoid enemy defences. In the anti-tank role it can deliver cluster bombs or unguided rockets, or can carry a range of sophisticated air-to-surface missiles including the widely used AS-7 'Kerry'. 'Kerry' is believed to employ radio command guidance.

The Su-25 can use its cannon in the air-to-air role, and enemy helicopters would represent an important target. If attacked by an enemy fighter the

*Two Czech 'Frogfoot' aircraft, armed with underwing rocket pods and carrying litre fuel tanks. Blade antennas at the wingtips serve the defensive ECM system.*

# Battlefield Evaluation: comparing

## Sukhoi Su-25 'Frogfoot'

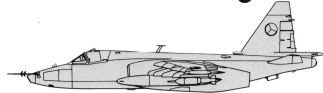

**Specification:**
**Length overall:** 14.5 m
**Wingspan:** 15.5 m
**Maximum speed at sea level:** 475 kt
**Combat radius lo-lo-lo:** 544 km
**Maximum weapon load:** 4,000 kg
**Take-off distance:** 450 m

The Su-25 is fast and highly manoeuvrable, with good range and endurance. It is tough and robust, yet simple to maintain, even with primitive support facilities. The aircraft is heavily armed and is well endowed with active and passive ECM equipment, allowing it to survive over the contemporary battlefield. It is fast enough to avoid ground fire, but slow enough for the pilot to be able to take in the tactical environment.

**Assessment**
**Manoeuvrability** ★★★★
**Rough field capability** ★★★★
**Robustness** ★★★★
**Worldwide users** ★★

*The 'Frogfoot' is ideally suited to the close air support role in Europe, flying low and fast.*

## BAe Harrier GR.Mk 3

**Specification:**
**Length overall:** 14.27 m
**Wingspan:** 7.70 m
**Maximum speed at sea level:** 634 kt
**Combat radius lo-lo-lo:** 370 km
**Maximum weapon load:** 3,629 kg
**Take-off distance:** vertical, or up to 305 m at max weight

The Harrier has an unparalleled ability to operate from dispersed, semi-prepared sites, using tiny strips of road or grass as its improvised runways. The aircraft is extremely manoeuvrable and very fast, with sufficient power to have outstanding acceleration even when fully laden, however, and can carry only a relatively small weapons load. Its avionics systems are extremely primitive and unreliable, although its superbly trained pilots make it a formidable fighting machine.

**Assessment**
**Manoeuvrability** ★★★★★
**Rough field capability** ★★★★★
**Robustness** ★★★★
**Worldwide users** ★

*The Harrier GR.Mk 3 is getting old, but remains a highly effective close support aircraft.*

## SEPECAT Jaguar

**Specification:**
**Length overall:** 16.83 m
**Wingspan:** 15.69 m
**Maximum speed at sea level:** 729 kt
**Combat radius lo-lo-lo:** 917 km
**Maximum weapon load:** 4,763 kg
**Take-off distance:** 565 m

The Jaguar is faster than the Su-25, and carries a heavier warload over a longer range. It is considerably less manoeuvrable, and is more suited to counter-air or interdiction missions than to close-air support or battlefield air interdiction duties. The nav-attack system carried by the Jaguar is second to none, permitting precision attacks on pinpoint targets, but its defensive avionics are much less impressive.

**Assessment**
**Manoeuvrability** ★★
**Rough field capability** ★★★★
**Robustness** ★★★★
**Worldwide users** ★★★★

*Jaguar remains a useful short-range strike aircraft. The long-range role is now performed by Tornado.*

Su-25 would rely mainly on its small size and outstanding manoeuvrability, but can carry a pair of AA-8 'Aphid' infra-red homing close-range air-to-air missiles on its outboard underwing pylons.

### Effective close support

'Frogfoot' is a potent and useful warplane, blooded in Afghanistan and now beginning to enter service in substantial numbers. It is likely to prove a much more effective close-support tool than the supersonic fighters and their derivatives currently in use in the role. This nimble, hard-hitting little aircraft seems set to win a similar reputation.

*Large twin braking parachutes give the 'Frogfoot' a very short landing run, allowing it to operate from small strips of road or even from improvised forward airstrips.*

# the 'Frogfoot' with its rivals

## BAe Hawk

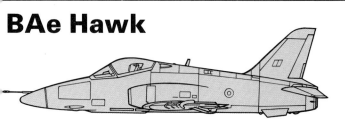

The BAe Hawk is a versatile advanced trainer with a useful light strike and air defence capability. The single-seat Hawk 200 is a dedicated combat version, with radar or FLIR and LRMTS in a re-profiled nose. Two 25-mm Aden cannon, also used in the Harrier GR.Mk 5, are installed internally, leaving the centreline pylon and four underwing stations free for the carriage of a variety of bombs or missiles.

**Specification:**
**Length overall:** 11.38 m
**Wingspan:** 9.39 m
**Maximum speed at sea level:** 560 kt
**Combat radius lo-lo-lo:** 998 km
**Maximum weapon load:** 3,084 kg
**Take-off distance:** 1,585 m

**Assessment**
Manoeuvrability ★★★★
Rough field capability ★
Robustness ★★★
Worldwide users ★★★★★

*The Hawk 200 is a successful close air support tool, with a particularly useful anti-helicopter capability.*

## Dassault-Breguet/ Dornier Alpha Jet

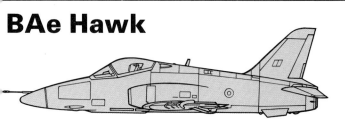

The Alpha Jet advanced trainer is available in a number of versions, and is used by some nations as a light attack aircraft. Luftwaffe Alpha Jets are inevitably flown as single-seaters, and are used almost exclusively in the close air support, weapons training and reconnaissance roles. Various expanded capability attack variants are also available.

**Specification:**
**Length overall:** 13.23 m
**Wingspan:** 9.11 m
**Maximum speed at sea level:** 540 kt
**Combat radius lo-lo-lo:** 390 km
**Maximum weapon load:** 2,500 kg
**Take-off distance:** 370 m

**Assessment**
Manoeuvrability ★★★
Rough field capability ★
Robustness ★
Worldwide users ★★★★

*The Luftwaffe uses its Alpha Jets in the close air support and weapons training roles.*

## Fairchild A-10A Thunderbolt II

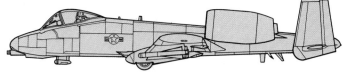

The A-10A is in a class of its own. No other close support aircraft can rival the A-10A in terms of the weight of armour carried, redundancy of systems, resistance to battle damage, and in terms of sheer low-level manoeuvrability. The A-10A is, however, very slow, and is being withdrawn from Europe in favour of the faster A-7 Strikefighter.

**Specification:**
**Length overall:** 16.26 m
**Wingspan:** 17.53 m
**Maximum speed at sea level:** 381 kt
**Combat radius lo-lo-lo:** 463 km
**Maximum weapon load:** 7,257 kg
**Take-off distance:** 1,219 m

**Assessment**
Manoeuvrability ★★★★
Rough field capability ★★
Robustness ★★★★
Worldwide users ★

*Highly manoeuvrable and heavily armoured, the A-10 is too slow to survive over the Central Front.*

# Tear into it with a T-62

**Tanks are noisy and cramped, dirty and dangerous, and the Soviet T-62 is worse than most. In fact, it has earned a reputation as one of the most uncomfortable combat vehicles in service today.** Entering production in 1961, it was the leading Soviet battle tank by the late 1960s and formed the backbone of the Warsaw Pact armies deployed against Western Europe during the 1970s. In the last few years it has been eclipsed by the T-64/72/80 series, but it is still in widespread service with the Warsaw Pact and forms the main strength of Arab armies in the Middle East.

The T-62 packs a formidable punch and has reasonable armour protection and good cross-country performance. Its low silhouette makes it a much smaller target than its US contemporary, the M60, and it weighs just under 40 tonnes. But these impressive performance figures are purchased at the expense of crew comfort, which means that the T-62's performance in reality often falls short of its theoretical capability.

## New army gun

The T-62 introduced a new gun into the Soviet army, the U-5TS 115-mm smoothbore which fires three main types of ammunition. HVAPFSDS (Hyper Velocity Armour Piercing Fin Stabilized Discarding Sabot) is the primary anti-tank round, consisting of a steel core penetrator that travels at over 1,600 metres per second – faster than the eye can follow – and will penetrate any tank armour within 2,000 metres.

HEATFS (High Explosive Anti Tank Fin Stabilized) is now the secondary anti-tank round, although it was originally the main reason for the introduction of a smoothbore gun. HEAT relies on creating an explosive jet of molten metal, which burns through a target's armour; but the spin imparted to a shell fired from a rifled gun to make it more accurate prevents the jet from forming properly. The answer is to use an unrifled gun and attach pop-up fins to the shell to keep it on a steady trajectory.

*A Soviet T-62 in Afghanistan with interesting modifications: note the horseshoe-shaped extra armour on the turret front, similar to the add-on armour recently fitted to British Chieftains.*

A smoothbore gun offers many advantages over the traditional rifled gun. The barrel can be lighter and mounted further forward in a stabilized mounting, and it is actually more efficient in imparting to the shell the energy created by the explosion of the cartridge. This allows a smaller cartridge to be used and hence a smaller cradle, mounting and recoil system, with important savings of weight and space.

## Highly capable

By fitting a new and revolutionary gun to the T-62, the Soviets planned to produce a tank easily capable of knocking out the M48s, M60s and Centurions then facing their armies in central Europe. In the opinion of some Israelis who have used T-62s captured from Syria and Egypt, the 115-mm smoothbore is a good tank gun, not inferior to the L7 105-mm rifled gun widely used in NATO. However, for

*A T-62 of the Afghan army shelters behind a sangar. Although leaving front-line Soviet service, the T-62 remains widely used by Soviet allies, but needs a good crew to be an effective MBT.*

all the power of its main armament, the T-62 fails in many other respects.

The commander, gunner and loader are squashed together in the turret,

prey to a number of disagreeable design features. There is a multitude of switches, clips, racks and assorted equipment, all with sharp corners which you cannot avoid banging into when the tank is moving at speed.

After the gun fires, the spent shell case is dropped into a tray which presents it to an ejection port in the turret rear and flings it out at high speed.

*An Iraqi T-62 kicks up the sand as it clatters across the desert. The T-62 is designed for action in a cold climate: it has a good heating system and is light enough to travel over ice 72 or more centimetres thick. Unfortunately, it has seen most of its action in the Middle East, where none of these advantages count and all of its weaknesses come into prominence.*

*Left: T-62s are carried by monstrous MAZ 537 tank transports. Note the ditching log carried underneath the big external fuel tank on the rear hull. Soviet diesel fuel has a high flashpoint, and tests in the USA show that even a white phosphorus round is unlikely to ignite it.*

Unfortunately, the jarring vibrations caused by the T-62 lurching over rough terrain tend to spoil the alignment of the tray and the ejection port. If this happens, the big brass case ricochets back into the turret. The commander's seat has a shield to protect his back, but the gunner and loader have no protection.

Since World War II tank guns have become able to shoot at longer and longer ranges, but most tank battles have been fought at much the same distances. Even in the 1973 Arab-Israeli war, which took place in very open terrain, engagement ranges were usually under 1,000 metres, which sets the latest claims for accurate tank gunnery at over 5,000 metres in their proper context.

## Long-range disadvantage

In a future war in central Europe it is unlikely that combat ranges would be substantially higher. The Soviets recognised this and the T-62's armament is optimised for close-range fighting; at over 1,500 metres the HVAPFSDS round loses enough velocity to impair both accuracy and penetration. At longer ranges or in gusty weather conditions the wind acts on the shell's fins.

Unfortunately, since any modern tank can knock out another if they are only a kilometre or so apart, the winner is the tank that hits first. In 'quick draw situations', as the US Army dubs such encounters, the T-62 is at a disadvantage. Its optical rangefinding equipment is prone to error and, although this is being replaced by a

# Inside the T-62

The T-62 is widely used in the Warsaw Pact and the Middle East, although most Soviet first-line tank divisions now use the T-64/72/80 types of MBT. The 1973 Arab-Israeli war revealed some serious weaknesses in the T-62: its 115-mm gun takes too long to reload, the turret traverse is slow, and the gun has limited depression. This is a T-62A, distinguished from the original T-62 by having a second cupola above the loader's position.

**Driver**
Driving the T-62 is a nightmare: the tiny driver's compartment is stiflingly hot and airless. You have five forward and one reverse gears, and have to double de-clutch to shift them. At any sort of speed the vibration is severe, and the inadequate suspension makes you feel every jolt as the tank crashes across the countryside.

**External fuel cell**
The T-62 carries three of these along the top of the hull on the right hand side; they contain a total of 285 litres of fuel. Internal tank contain 675 litres.

**U-5TS 115-mm smoothbore gun**
This has a shorter effective range than the NATO 105-mm gun, but is highly accurate at up to 1500 metres. The flat trajectory of the BR-5 HVAPFSDS means you do not have to worry about elevation up to this range.

**Glacis**
This is protected by 102 mm of armour sloped at 54° on the lower half and 60° on the upper. A shell on a flat trajectory thus has about 200 mm of armour to punch its way through.

*Syrian T-62s knocked out during the tank battles on the Golan Heights in 1973. If you are in a T-62 which is hit and catches fire, the good news is that the ethylene-bromide fire suppression system cuts in automatically. The bad news is that the gas is highly poisonous and you must get out fast.*

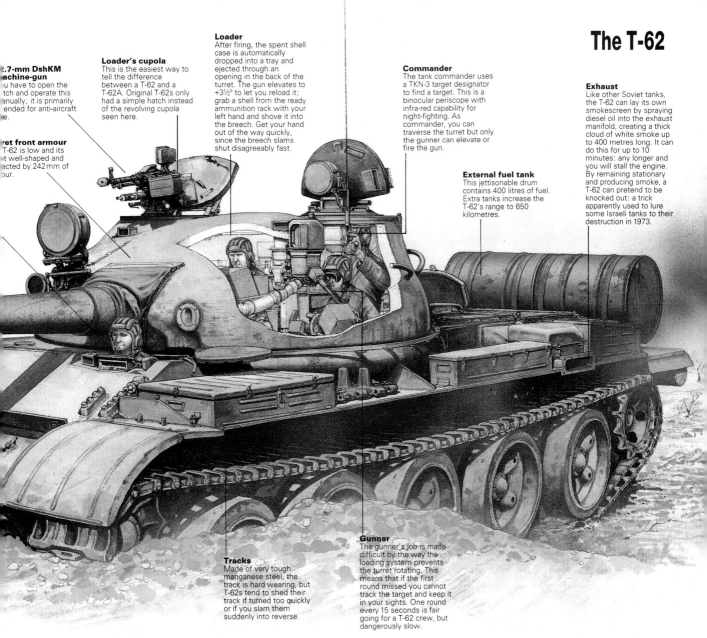

**.7-mm DshKM achine-gun**
u have to open the tch and operate this anually; it is primarily ended for anti-aircraft e.

**Loader's cupola**
This is the easiest way to tell the difference between a T-62 and a T-62A. Original T-62s only had a simple hatch instead of the revolving cupola seen here.

**Loader**
After firing, the spent shell case is automatically dropped into a tray and ejected through an opening in the back of the turret. The gun elevates to +3½° to let you reload it; grab a shell from the ready ammunition rack with your left hand and shove it into the breech. Get your hand out of the way quickly, since the breech slams shut disagreeably fast.

**Commander**
The tank commander uses a TKN-3 target designator to find a target. This is a binocular periscope with infra-red capability for night-fighting. As commander, you can traverse the turret but only the gunner can elevate or fire the gun.

**Exhaust**
Like other Soviet tanks, the T-62 can lay its own smokescreen by spraying diesel oil into the exhaust manifold, creating a thick cloud of white smoke up to 400 metres long. It can do this for up to 10 minutes: any longer and you will stall the engine. By remaining stationary and producing smoke, a T-62 can pretend to be knocked out: a trick apparently used to lure some Israeli tanks to their destruction in 1973.

**External fuel tank**
This jettisonable drum contains 400 litres of fuel. Extra tanks increase the T-62's range to 650 kilometres.

**ret front armour**
T-62 is low and its t well-shaped and ected by 242mm of ur.

**Tracks**
Made of very tough manganese steel, the track is hard wearing, but T-62s tend to shed their track if turned too quickly or if you slam them suddenly into reverse.

**Gunner**
The gunner's job is made difficult by the way the loading system prevents the turret rotating. This means that if the first round missed you cannot track the target and keep it in your sights. One round every 15 seconds is fair going for a T-62 crew, but dangerously slow.

laser rangefinder, the main armament cannot track a moving target while it is being loaded. So if you miss with the first round you must wait to correct your aim while the loader frantically chambers another shell.

## Moving targets

Tanks, like all military equipment, are dependent on the ability of the soldiers using them. The T-62s fielded in large numbers by the Arab armies in the Yom Kippur war met with bloody defeat after the heady success of the early days'. Syrian and Egyptian crews were simply no match for the highly competent Israelis, and the use of stereotyped and utterly predictable text-book tactics compounded the problem.

But although the Golan Heights were left littered with burnt-out T-62s, the Israelis equipped at least one brigade of their army with captured ones and found the armament perfectly adequate. The human

engineering of the T-62 could not fail to arouse criticism but, given a good crew, it can still be an effective MBT. The Arab and, to a lesser extent, the Warsaw Pact problem is that poorly-trained crews exacerbate the existing weaknesses of the tank and turn a well-balanced fighting vehicle into a lumbering deathtrap.

For all its problems the T-62 is by no means a failure: its introduction gave the Soviets superiority in NBC protection. Triggered by a sensor detecting the pulse of radiation generated by a nuclear weapon, the T-62's NBC system automatically shuts all openings and alerts the crew by cutting off the engine. An over-pressure system

*A T-62 of the Iraqi army moves into a prepared hull-down position. In defence, a Soviet-trained T-62 crew would hold fire until the target was within 1500 metres or less.*

*An Iraqi loader mans the 12.7-mm anti-aircraft machine-gun: a powerful and very reliable weapon, but you need a good concentration of them to bring down modern aircraft.*

stops radioactive dust from circulating inside the tank, and an anti-radiation lining protects the whole crew compartment. In fact, the vehicle is not well protected against chemical weapons and using the gun breaks the NBC seal, but it is good enough for Soviet doctrine to envisage T-62s speeding through contaminated areas to win tactical advantage.

### Snorkelling preparation

The T-62 can snorkel across a river as long as the bottom is reasonably flat, but this needs engineering preparation to work successfully, otherwise the tank cannot climb out on the other side or loses its sense of direc-

# Battlefield Evaluation: comparing

## T-62

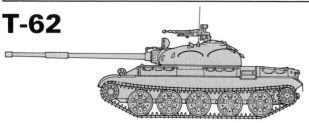

The T-62's 115-mm smoothbore gun substantially improved the firepower of Soviet armoured units; it is far superior to the old 100-mm weapon carried by the T-54/55 series. However, the T-62 never replaced the T-54/55 as the standard Warsaw Pact MBT and has not proved as successful. It was never the equal of the American M60 or the Centurion as modified by the Israelis, but its poor performance in the Yom Kippur war was largely due to the poor quality of Syrian tank crew.

**Specification:**
**Crew:** 4
**Combat weight:** 40 tonnes
**Road speed:** 50 km/h
**Power-to-weight ratio:** 14.5 hp/tonne
**Length:** 6.63 m
**Height:** 2.4 m
**Armament:** 1×115-mm smoothbore gun; 1×12.7-mm and 1×7.62-mm machine-guns

**Assessment**
| | |
|---|---|
| Firepower | ★★★★ |
| Protection | ★★★ |
| Age | ★★★★★ |
| Worldwide users | ★★★★ |

*Combat experience has exposed all of the T-62's weaknesses but revealed few of its strengths.*

## M60

The M60 is better protected than the T-62, and the standard NATO 105-mm tank gun is certainly the equal of the Soviet 115-mm weapon; and better fire control systems can make it superior. The M60 is better engineered than the T-62, which is manufactured to the usually low Soviet standards, and mechanical reliability is greater.

**Specification:**
**Crew:** 4
**Combat weight:** 52 tonnes
**Road speed:** 48 km/h
**Power-to-weight ratio:** 14 hp/tonne
**Length:** 6.9 m
**Height:** 3.27 m
**Armament:** 1×105-mm gun; 1×12.7-mm and 1×7.62-mm machine-guns

**Assessment**
| | |
|---|---|
| Firepower | ★★★★ |
| Protection | ★★★★ |
| Age | ★★★★★ |
| Worldwide users | ★★★★★ |

*The M60 series tanks are marginally superior to T-62s and a lot less uncomfortable for the crew.*

## M48

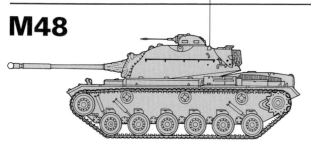

Compared with the T-62, the M48 was under-armed and under-powered: its 90-mm gun lacked the penetrative power of the Soviet 115-mm HVAPFSDS round, and the T-62 has superior battlefield mobility. The large turret is protected by 110 mm of armour, but the T-62's turret is better shaped to deflect a shell and has 170 mm of armour plate. In other areas the two tanks are similarly protected.

**Specification:**
**Crew:** 4
**Combat weight:** 47 tonnes
**Road speed:** 48 km/h
**Power-to-weight ratio:** 17 hp/tonne
**Length:** 6.8 m
**Height:** 3.1 m
**Armament:** 1×90-mm gun; 1×12.7-mm and 1×7.62-mm machine-guns

**Assessment**
| | |
|---|---|
| Firepower | ★★★ |
| Protection | ★★★ |
| Age | ★★★★★ |
| Worldwide users | ★★ |

*Poorly armed and underpowered, early model M48s were inferior to the T-55 and T-62.*

tion and slowly circles around underwater.

NATO forces have the advantage of having acquired large numbers of T-62s in the wake of the Yom Kippur war, and the vehicle has been exhaustively analysed. Its hunched, sinister silhouette appears less of a menace when its weaknesses have been exposed, and the lesson is obvious that the ruthless subordination of crew comfort to tactical advantage is not necessarily effective. On the other hand, every NATO tank has its problems, and to write Soviet MBTs off as inferior, unreliable vehicles manned by incapable conscripts is the height of foolishness.

*A column of T-62s on winter exercises in the USSR. Whereas US M60s need to regularly run their engines during the night and thus betray their position, the T-62 has a compressed air system for a cold start and a pre-heater.*

# the T-62 with its rivals

## T-54/55

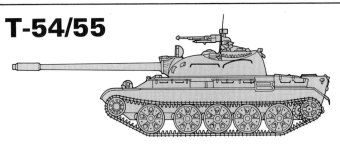

The T-54/55 series of Main Battle Tanks remains in widespread use, and many countries are offering modernisation kits. The main weakness of the T-54/55 was always its main armament. If this is replaced by a Royal Ordnance 105-mm rifled gun, a laser fire control system and some automotive parts, you have a very cost-effective MBT.

**Specification:**
**Crew:** 4
**Combat weight:** 36 tonnes
**Road speed:** 50 km/h
**Power-to-weight ratio:** 16 hp/tonne
**Length:** 6.45 m
**Height:** 2.4 m
**Armament:** 1×100-mm gun; 1 or 2×7.62-mm and 1×12.7-mm machine-guns

**Assessment**
Firepower ★★
Protection ★★★
Age ★★★★★
Worldwide users ★★★★★

*The T-54/55 series tanks have proved remarkably long-lived considering the crudeness of the design.*

## AMX-30

Appearing in French service several years after the Soviets introduced the T-62, the AMX-30 is lighter and less well armoured. On the other hand, it is armed with an effective 105-mm gun and a co-axial 20-mm cannon for chewing up APCs and soft vehicles. It is a more agile tank than the T-62 but, like the Soviet tank, it is obsolete when compared with Leopard 2 or T-80.

**Specification:**
**Crew:** 4
**Combat weight:** 36 tonnes
**Road speed:** 50 km/h
**Power-to-weight ratio:** 20 hp/tonne
**Length:** 6.59 m
**Height:** 2.29 m
**Armament:** 1×105-mm gun; 1×20-mm cannon; 1×7.62-mm machine-gun

**Assessment**
Firepower ★★★★
Protection ★★
Age ★★★★
Worldwide users ★★

*The AMX-30 has excellent battlefield mobility and is armed with a co-axial 20-mm cannon and 105-mm gun.*

## Centurion

The Centurion is one of the best tanks ever produced by Britain, and in Israeli hands it has met and defeated the T-62. Centurion prototypes were sent to Germany in 1945 but were not in time to see any action; today, up-armoured, up-gunned and re-engined, they are still highly potent MBTs. Used by Israel, South Africa, Denmark, Sweden, the Netherlands and in various engineer roles by the British Army, Centurions are enormous fun to drive.

**Specification:** Mk 13
**Crew:** 4
**Combat weight:** 51 tonnes
**Road speed:** 34 km/h
**Power-to-weight ratio:** 12.5 hp/tonne
**Length:** 7.8 m
**Height:** 3 m
**Armament:** 1×105-mm gun; 1×12.7-mm and 2×7.62-mm machine-guns

**Assessment**
Firepower ★★★★
Protection ★★★
Age ★★★★★
Worldwide users ★★★

*In Israeli hands the Centurion has become an extremely successful Main Battle Tank.*

# Blast them with the MLRS

*Until recently, only the West German army shared the enthusiasm of the Soviets for multiple rocket-launchers. On the Eastern Front in World War II both sides supplemented their conventional artillery with massed rocket fire, which enables you to blast the enemy with a savage intensity.* In a few seconds a battery of rocket-launchers can dump an incredible quantity of explosive on a target and, if it catches a unit unprepared, the results are catastrophic.

Multiple rocket-launchers are ideal offensive weapons systems, able to deluge enemy defences immediately prior to an attack. They are ideal for the delivery of intense concentrations of smoke to conceal your advance, or chemical ammunition such as blood-agents which are far more lethal if delivered all in one go rather than steadily built up by a conventional artillery barrage.

These are the primary tasks of the Soviet multiple rocket-launchers, but

The MLRS is fitted to a modified M2 Bradley chassis, the Self-Propelled Loader Launcher (SPLL) vehicle. This has excellent cross-country mobility.

Above: Elevated to firing position. MLRS can fire 12 independently-aimed rockets in 90 seconds then move rapidly to a new position.

NATO rockets have a different objective. They are part of NATO's comprehensive anti-tank plan: yet another weapon system tasked with stopping massed Soviet armour from crashing through to the Rhine.

The West German Light Artillery Rocket System, or LARS, is mounted on the highly manoeuvrable seventon cross-country Magirus-Jupiter. A variety of munitions, including High Explosive, smoke, incendiary, anti-vehicle and anti-armour can be fired often in a "mixed-bag" assortment. More recently the AT-1 Pandora minelet, devastating against soft-skinned vehicles and dismounted infantry, has entered the arsenal.

Although LARS seemed very advanced when first introduced, the evolution in the early 1970s of a new generation of Soviet self-propelled artillery coupled with the introduction of new tank armour soon made it obsolete.

### The way ahead

The 122-mm 2S1 howitzer, introduced into Soviet tank and BMP-equipped regiments from 1974, could easily outrange LARS, and the armour plating on the T-64/72 main battle tanks then entering service with GSFG (Group Soviet Forces Germany) was such that the comparatively light 110-mm LARS rocket would have to

score a near direct hit to do the tank serious damage.

The need for a larger, far longer ranged and more accurate rocket was emphasised by a change in tactical thinking then taking place within NATO. Previously NATO had concentrated its resources on the destruction of the enemy in the front line, but it now emphasises the importance of striking deeper into the enemy rear to disrupt his command, control, communications and intelligence network (known in NATO jargon as $C^3I$). Whereas low-flying fighter ground-attack aircraft could carry out this role 50 km and more behind the FEBA (Forward Edge of Battle Area), they

*The Multiple Launch Rocket System is a spectacular sight in action. Because it is so easy to detect its firing position, MLRS batteries will have to 'shoot and scoot': fire a rapid salvo then drive quickly away before the enemy can bring down fire on their position.*

could not operate closer to the front line without sustaining severe losses from Soviet anti-aircraft systems. What NATO needed was a long-range rocket.

### MLRS

The resultant MLRS, or multiple launch rocket system, entered service with the 1st Infantry Division (Mechanized) at Fort Riley, Kansas, in 1983. By the autumn of 1986 the US army had 337 launchers operational, while the United Kingdom, France and West Germany had others on order.

Mounted on a tracked self-propelled loader-launcher vehicle (SPLL) based on the M2 Bradley chassis, MLRS has the mobility and speed to keep up with armoured units. Its ability to halt, fire 12 independently-aimed missiles and withdraw, all in the space of 90 seconds, makes it a formidable weapon.

The crew of three (commander, driver and gunner) can reload with two rocket containers, each with six pre-loaded tubes, without leaving the protection of their armoured cab. Each vehicle is equipped with its own inertial navigation system and computer which can be independently programmed by a front-line forward observation officer direct, thus saving considerable time. The crew can rip-

*MLRS fires off a single rocket which still produces a massive blast (or 'launch signature'). Originally, multiple rocket launchers relied on massive salvoes to make up for the relative inaccuracy of individual rockets. MLRS's 227-mm rockets are much more accurate and carry complicated sub-munitions.*

*The sight of an MLRS on the move will be increasingly common in Europe as NATO armies receive their launchers. If the performance of the rockets lives up to expectations MLRS will play an important role in European defence.*

ple-fire from two to 12 rounds in less than one minute, the fire control automatically re-aiming after each shot.

## Munitions

MLRS is designed to fire any of three types of submunition: bomblets, anti-armour minelets and guided sub-missiles. There is a suggestion that a binary chemical warhead may be under development, but at the moment this is a matter of pure conjecture.

The M-77 bomblet, presently on order by the United Kingdom, would be of greatest use against unprotected soft-skinned vehicles, armoured personnel carriers and towed artillery. Six hundred and forty-four bomblets are packed into each 159-kg missile, so each MLRS is capable of simultaneously discharging 7,728 bomblets over a given area. To give some indication of the potential havoc this could cause, it has been said that a battery of launchers could obliterate an area the size of four football pitches and that only two launchers would be required to destroy an enemy gun battery dug in up to 30 km away.

Although the bomblet has obvious advantages when employed against lightly-protected targets, it would be of little use against massed armour, and for these targets the AT-2 is being developed. Each missile consists of seven independent warheads or sub-munitions.

Approximately 1 km from the general target the main warhead disintegrates, releasing the warheads, which locate their own targets, falling with the aid of a parachute onto the victim's lightly-protected roof. When this concept reaches the production stage and deployment it will clearly revolutionise the armoured battle of the future.

## Target location

No matter how accurate a weapon – and the MLRS is among the most accurate in production – it will only hit its target if properly aimed. Targets 30 km away are well beyond line of sight, and alternative methods of target location must be found. Traditionally spotter aircraft or helicopters were used in this role, but modern anti-aircraft weapons make this impractical. Most countries have turned to the RPV (remotely piloted vehicle) to provide the solution. Such "aircraft", or more correctly drones, are either pre-programmed or controlled by radio impulses generated from the safety of the user's front line. "Real time" signals are transmitted back to the user for translation into fire missions.

The British Army is at the moment developing Phoenix, an advanced RPV, to operate in conjunction with the MLRS in "Depth Fire" regiments, which will ultimately take over responsibilities for heavy regiment counter-battery warfare from the existing 175-mm M-107 batteries. Although this creation has not been without its hardships (for instance, it led to disbandment of 94 (Locating Regiment) RA, which had served in the West German town of Celle for over 35 years) it is hoped that by the time the MLRS and Phoenix are operational the Gunners will be fully able to exploit their vast potential.

**Cab**
The danger from rocket fumes is a serious problem for rocket-launcher crews. MLRS has an overpressure system in the cab to keep the fumes out, as well as a full NBC system.

**Commander**

**Gunner**
MLRS can operate with only two crew, and it is theoretically possible for one man to load and fire the system alone.

**Fire control display**

**Fire control**
The fire control system has to relay the MLRS after it has fired a rocket, since the massive blast moves the vehicle's position.

**Driver**

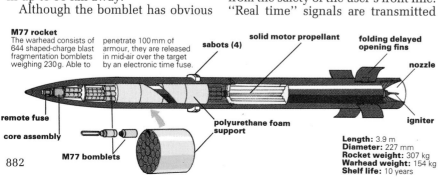

**M77 rocket**
The warhead consists of 644 shaped-charge blast fragmentation bomblets weighing 230 g. Able to penetrate 100 mm of armour, they are released in mid-air over the target by an electronic time fuse.

sabots (4)

solid motor propellant

folding delayed opening fins

nozzle

igniter

remote fuse

core assembly

M77 bomblets

polyurethane foam support

**Length:** 3.9 m
**Diameter:** 227 mm
**Rocket weight:** 307 kg
**Warhead weight:** 154 kg
**Shelf life:** 10 years

# Inside the MLRS

In a future European war the main role of MLRS would be rapidly to lay down minefields in the path of advancing enemy armour. Using the AT-2 anti-tank mine, MLRS can sow 336 mines over an area 1000×400 metres in one minute.

**Rockets**
MLRS fires three basic types of rocket: one dispensing anti-personnel mines, one dropping anti-tank mines, and one chemical warhead (used only by the US Army). In 1985 the US Army announced that it is planning a fourth warhead called SADARM. This will carry 6 anti-tank missiles which will independently seek out their targets and fire a hypersonic velocity penetrator slug through the tank's top armour.

**Blow-off covers**
The rockets are hermetically sealed in their tubes and have a shelf life of 10 years.

**Boom extension actuators**

**Launch pod**
The rockets are contained in fibreglass tubes within an aluminium six-pack weighing 2.27 tonnes. MLRS batteries are supported by HEMTT 8-wheel drive trucks, each carrying four launch pods.

**Launch container**

**Aluminium armour**
This protects the crew from small-arms fire and shell splinters, but cannot save the vehicle from a direct hit by shells or cannon.

**Elevation actuators**

## The future

Production of the MLRS has now become an international concern. Representatives of five countries – LTVB Aerospace and Defence of the United States, Aérospatiale of France, Diehl of West Germany, Hunting Engineering of Great Britain and SNIA-BPD of Italy – are now marketing the system worldwide and already have 30 interested parties as varied as Greece, Saudi Arabia and Pakistan.

The United States has already

*Firing in response to signals from remote-controlled reconnaissance aircraft (RPVs), MLRS is highly effective in silencing enemy artillery batteries.*

# Battlefield Evaluation: comparing

## MLRS

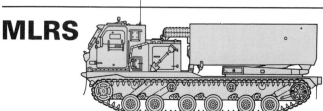

The Multiple Launch Rocket System began as a US Army project following the Soviet lead in multiple rocket-launchers. European interest has been strong, with West Germany, Italy, France and the UK all planning to deploy the system. The British Army is planning to equip three Royal Artillery Regiments with MLRS, replacing elderly Abbot SP 105-mm guns in BAOR. MLRS is an excellent system with tremendous firepower, but whereas the Soviets use rockets to supplement their conventional artillery, NATO forces seem to be using rockets to replace obsolete guns.

**Specification:**
**Crew:** 3
**Combat weight:** 26 tonnes
**No. of rockets:** 12
**Rocket calibre:** 227 mm
**Warhead weight:** variable
**Range:** 30-40 km depending on rocket type

**Assessment**
Firepower ★★★★
Accuracy ★★★★
Age ★★
Worldwide users ★★★

**MLRS introduces high technology to the previously simple concept of the multiple rocket-launcher.**

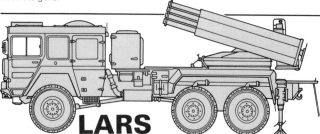

## LARS

West Germany was the first NATO power to follow the Soviet lead and introduce modern multiple rocket launchers. LARS entered service in 1969; a simple system based on 6×6 trucks, each Army division received a battery of eight launchers. A wide variety of rocket types are now used, including a parachute-retarded anti-tank mine dispenser and HE fragmentation warheads. New improved LARS II features better fire control systems and is mounted on a MAN truck chassis.

**Specification:**
**Crew:** 3
**Combat weight:** 7 tonnes
**No. of warheads:** 36
**Rocket calibre:** 110 mm
**Warhead weight:** unknown
**Range:** 14 km

**Assessment**
Firepower ★★★
Accuracy ★★★
Age ★★★★
Worldwide users ★

**LARS was the first NATO MRLS, introduced by the West Germans in the late 1960s.**

## BM21

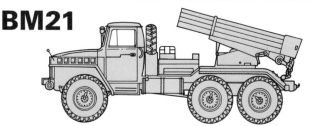

The BM21 entered service over 25 years ago, and remains in front-line service throughout the Warsaw Pact. It is a far more cost-effective system than MLRS and its relative simplicity allows the Soviets to manufacture and deploy the BM21 in awesome numbers. The Soviets value their rocket batteries for their ability to dump more explosive on target with a single salvo than an equivalent force of artillery firing for 30 minutes.

**Specification:**
**Crew:** 6
**Combat weight:** 11.5 tonnes
**No. of rockets:** 40
**Rocket calibre:** 122 mm
**Warhead weight:** 19.4
**Range:** 20 km

**Assessment**
Firepower ★★★★★
Accuracy ★★
Age ★★★★★
Worldwide users ★★★★★

**The Soviet BM21 is a far cruder weapon than MLRS, which allows the Soviets to use huge numbers of them.**

fielded 15 MLRS batteries within the USA, in West Germany and in Korea, and has reserves of over 100,000 rockets. The first European systems are expected to enter service by 1988, with exports following three to four years later.

The MLRS has the potential to revolutionise land warfare over the next decade and is one of the most important pieces of equipment to enter service since the end of World War II.

*MLRS deployed for action during exercises in West Germany. Able to create instant minefields with the bomblets dispensed by the M77 rocket, MLRS can be an important anti-armour weapon.*

# the MLRS with its rivals

## BM24

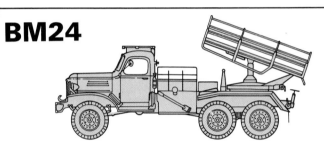

This is a Soviet system dating from the 1950s, no longer in frontline service with the Warsaw Pact but still used in the Middle East and still maintained by reserve formations in Eastern Europe. The Israelis captured so many from the Arabs that they now make their own rockets for the BM24. These are more effective than the originals, although they have slightly less range.

**Specification:**
**Crew:** 6
**Combat weight:** 9.2 tonnes
**No. of rockets:** 12
**Rocket calibre:** 240 mm
**Warhead weight:** 47 kg
**Range:** 11 km

**Assessment**
| | |
|---|---|
| Firepower | ***** |
| Accuracy | ** |
| Age | ***** |
| Worldwide users | ** |

*The Israelis captured large numbers of BM24s and now use them themselves.*

## Valkiri

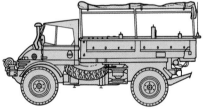

The South African Army has encountered BM21s in Angola, and recognised the value of a simple weapons system able to suddenly deluge an enemy position with high explosive. Valkiri was developed in South Africa and entered service five years ago. Fitted to a 4×4 SAMIL truck chassis, Valkiri is highly mobile and doubly useful in bush warfare where the morale effect of multiple rocket-launchers can be devastatingly effective.

**Specification:**
**Crew:** 2
**Combat weight:** 6.4 tonnes
**No. of rockets:** 24
**Rocket calibre:** 127 mm
**Warhead weight:** unknown
**Range:** 22 km

**Assessment**
| | |
|---|---|
| Firepower | *** |
| Accuracy | *** |
| Age | * |
| Worldwide users | * |

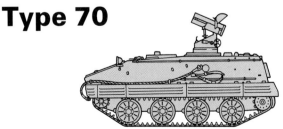

*South Africa has recently introduced Valkiri after facing BM21s in Angola.*

## Type 70

China's rapidly-developing military industries have produced several multiple rocket-launcher systems. The Type 70 is mounted on the chassis of a YM531 armoured personnel carrier, and saw action in the 1979 border fighting with Vietnam. They operate in six vehicle batteries attached to Chinese armoured divisions. A truck-mounted version, the Type 63, operates with infantry divisions.

**Specification:**
**Crew:** 6
**Combat weight:** 13.4 tonnes
**No. of rockets:** 19
**Rocket calibre:** 130 mm
**Warhead weight:** 14.7 kg
**Range:** 10 km

**Assessment**
| | |
|---|---|
| Firepower | *** |
| Accuracy | ** |
| Age | ** |
| Worldwide users | * |

*The Chinese Type 70 is available on a modified APC chassis or on a 4×4 lorry.*

# Escape and Evasion in Hostile Territory

*There are two types of evasion: long-term and short-term. The long-term evader is likely to be a PoW who has escaped from a camp inside enemy territory or has ejected from a fighter-bomber aircraft or become detached from a deep penetration patrol. Short-term evaders, however, can be on the run almost anywhere.* They can be recently-captured PoWs who have just escaped. They may be men who have become detached from a night patrol when it was 'bumped' in the darkness. They can be the survivors of a position that has been attacked and neutralised by superior forces.

The distinction between the two groups is that the short-term evaders may be armed and carrying equipment that will assist them, but they will be playing everything by ear – they will have no escape plan. The long-term evaders have the problem that they are often hundreds of miles from friendly forces and are enclosed in a PoW camp.

*Paratroopers taken prisoner are searched by SAS personnel at the end of an Escape and Evasion exercise prior to the next phase, tactical questioning. Note that their boots have been removed.*

## Points to remember

**1** In any future conventional war in Europe, evasion will be essential: modern tactics make surrendering a very difficult option. Warsaw Pact forces are not renowned for their fair treatment of PoWs.

**2** If you are captured, the sooner you escape the better. The further down the line you go, the more thoroughly you will be searched. More kit will be taken off you, and the ground will become more unfamiliar.

**3** You may not get any second chances; capture could mean death. Do not take risks.

**4** Preparation is essential. Lessons learned must be applied: E & E kit must be carried on all operations – on you, not in your Bergen – and you must be skilled in its use.

**5** Proficiency in unarmed combat is a considerable advantage, not only for physically resisting capture but also for promoting the right mental attitude of self-reliance.

They do, however, have time to plan and prepare clothing or equipment to assist them. Crucially, they can produce civilian clothes if the appearance of the locals will allow them to blend as civilians. If, however, their captors are physically very different then disguise is no assistance.

Short-term evasion is best conducted by small groups of about four men – larger numbers are hard to conceal, while smaller groups do not offer the protection and support nor the numbers to mount guard in a hide. So if there are more than four, you should divide up with group leaders – in this way, if some of you are captured, others may evade and exfiltrate to friendly forces.

## Wild food

Evasion in a temperate environment is easiest in early autumn, when fruits, nuts and fungi are available and the weather is not too cold. The most difficult time to evade is during deep winter or even very early spring: it is cold, and there is very little natural food about.

Unless you are fighting in one of the great wild temperate areas of the world such as Canada or deep in the USSR, temperate areas usually have a civilian population, which means you can try to get hold of their food. But try to avoid any contact with the local population – get to know the layout of a farm, for instance, so that you can steal food from the kitchen and vegetable garden or raid the hen coops or cow sheds. Beware: farms have dogs and a disturbed cow can make a lot of noise.

On one evasion exercise British special forces managed to extract some freshly laid eggs from a coop. When they started to boil them, they discovered that one of the eggs was made of china, placed by the farmer to encourage the chickens to lay.

## Bury the bones

If you intend to catch and butcher a sheep, remember that they can run very fast. If you do catch one you will need to drain the blood into a stream and bury the offal and bones – farmers feel very strongly about their sheep. They will report stolen sheep and the location of fires and signs of butchery.

In conventional and unconventional war there are refugees who will

*Avoid this situation: the better option is to swim the river at night rather than risk a bridge. In rural areas those who operate a toll bridge will know all the locals, and you will be noticed.*

## A prisoner's fate

*In a tactical situation, prisoners may outnumber the captors, who can ill afford the manpower for prisoner escort. Wounded prisoners put an additional strain on resources. In short, the enemy may have plenty of good reasons for killing you as a prisoner.*

*In the picture on the right, a Vietnamese marine gives water to a captured VC who was badly wounded in the legs and abdomen. The prisoner said he had been forced from his home by the VC and used as an ammunition bearer. Below, 30 minutes later, the same prisoner is shot dead by another marine.*

have left their homes and there will be some food stocks. Enemy soldiers may ditch some of their rations, so it is worth checking their bivouac sites: you may find pieces of equipment that will assist your evasion efforts.

Corpses of friendly troops will also have water and rations, and a former friendly position is worth checking.

It is best to move by night – this allows you to check navigation from the stars or simply with your compass. Keep a simple orienteering-type compass in your combat jacket pocket: you live with what's in your Bergen, fight with what's on your belt and sur-

vive with what's in your pockets. This should include a compass as well as an escape map, a simple first aid kit and water purifying tablets. A good pocket knife will complete a kit that can be adapted according to the individual's priorities.

## Resting by day

With this kit, the evader moves at night – when it is cold – and rests up by day when it is warm. When resting up, avoid obvious locations, including the temptingly dry outbuildings on a farm.

Try to find a place where you can see approaching search parties and have an escape route. A small patch of scrub may be better than a wood; searchers are more likely to overlook the scrub. Remember that they may have dogs or cordon-and-search-teams in helicopters – you must camouflage from the air as well as from the ground.

In a temperate area such as Europe there are always polythene agricultural sacks in the fields. These are not

## A foraging raid
*Do not attempt a foraging raid unless you have exhausted all other means and are desperate. Apart from the obvious danger of being spotted, thefts from a farm will be discovered rapidly, perhaps while you are still nearby.*

**Hunger**
Your attitude, morale and will to survive will be affected after about four days without food. You will begin to suffer loss of weight, weakness, dizziness and blackouts, a slowed heart rate, a feeling of cold, and increased thirst.

*Short-term evaders prepare a shelter. It is vital that you have enough in your webbing to survive for several days; the habit of taking most of your kit out of your webbing for a night patrol could backfire badly if you are separated from it.*

**Personality**
This is perhaps the most important factor in an evasion situation. You must be decisive, adaptable, calm, optimistic but realistic, patient, able to improvise and to cope with isolation, and able to assess and predict the action of others.

**Stealing chickens**
The odd chicken may not be missed. But if you do not have specialist knowledge you shouldn't try to simulate a fox or dog raid; a gamekeeper will easily spot an amateur job and may put the enemy on your track.

**Stealing eggs**
If you are going to take eggs, take only a few. farmer knows that her sometimes do not lay properly, but he will no accept the loss of the contents of the hen co

**Care with sheep**
Hill sheep die on moorland all year round and a missing one is unlikely to be noticed; but be careful on the more closely monitored lowland farms. When gutting the sheep, always check the liver; it should not look grey or have any yellow patches when you cut into it.

only completely waterproof but are also a common sight and therefore good camouflage in themselves. Take care, however, to check what they have contained: some agricultural chemicals are toxic or at least harmful to humans. Farmers also use twine and cordage, and this is useful for building shelters and hides.

Remember, however, that farmers do not take kindly to having their hard-earned stock used by men on the run and they also have a very good

## Caves for cover

A boulder cave provides an excellent hide for an evader. Be careful to cover your tracks near the cave, and establish a strict trackplan so that disturbance to surrounding vegetation is kept to a

minimum. Do not try to improve the cover to the entrance too much, as farmers and game keepers will notice any changes in ground cover.

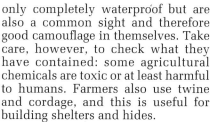

**Recce the target**
Carry out a careful reconnaissance, and plan the operation to cover every eventuality.

**Assess the risk**
Before going ahead, decide whether the likely takings are going to be worth the risks.

**Cover group**
This may be unconventional warfare, but do not discard conventional common sense. If you are operating as a four-man team, at least one person should cover the others from a position where he can see the whole target area and provide adequate warning of enemy or civilians.

**Plan your pickings**
You can take a lot of stuff that will last for several days, and move on rapidly, or stay in one place and steal small amounts that may not be noticed.

**Take your chances**
You must be constantly on the look-out for things that could be useful. Work out how to use them later.

idea of the layout of their land. Anything that looks out of the ordinary will attract their attention and they may pass this on to the hunters who are trying to find you or your group.

### Civilian disguise

Disguise in civilian clothing can take various forms. At its simplest you can use a coat or mackintosh over your uniform to conceal its colour or pattern. Or you may be able to find civilian clothes that fit and look acceptable. If, however, you adopt this course remember that if you are captured in civilian clothes and have a weapon, many enemy soldiers and governments will see you as a terrorist and beyond the normal rules of war.

If you do opt for disguise you need a washing and shaving kit, since dirty or bearded civilians are more likely to attract attention even near a war zone. Avoid children; unlike adults, they are uninhibited about staring at strangers.

Even the most junior soldier is a useful member of his national armed forces. Also, your return to friendly forces increases your country's knowledge of enemy tactics and operations.

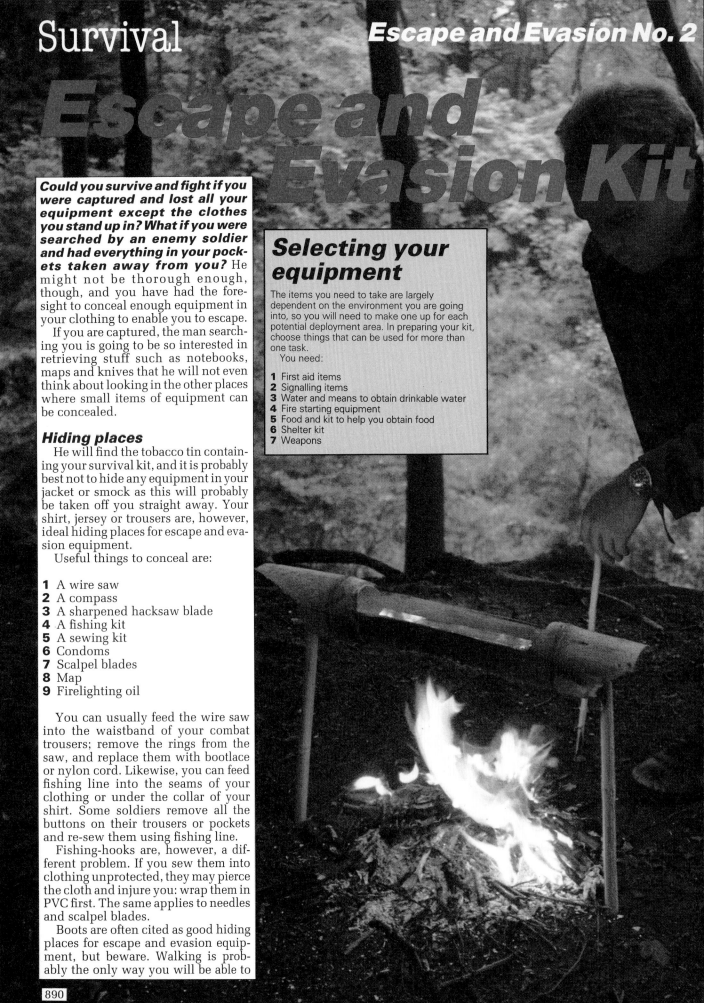

# Escape and Evasion Kit

**Could you survive and fight if you were captured and lost all your equipment except the clothes you stand up in? What if you were searched by an enemy soldier and had everything in your pockets taken away from you?** He might not be thorough enough, though, and you have had the foresight to conceal enough equipment in your clothing to enable you to escape.

If you are captured, the man searching you is going to be so interested in retrieving stuff such as notebooks, maps and knives that he will not even think about looking in the other places where small items of equipment can be concealed.

## Hiding places

He will find the tobacco tin containing your survival kit, and it is probably best not to hide any equipment in your jacket or smock as this will probably be taken off you straight away. Your shirt, jersey or trousers are, however, ideal hiding places for escape and evasion equipment.

Useful things to conceal are:

1 A wire saw
2 A compass
3 A sharpened hacksaw blade
4 A fishing kit
5 A sewing kit
6 Condoms
7 Scalpel blades
8 Map
9 Firelighting oil

You can usually feed the wire saw into the waistband of your combat trousers; remove the rings from the saw, and replace them with bootlace or nylon cord. Likewise, you can feed fishing line into the seams of your clothing or under the collar of your shirt. Some soldiers remove all the buttons on their trousers or pockets and re-sew them using fishing line.

Fishing-hooks are, however, a different problem. If you sew them into clothing unprotected, they may pierce the cloth and injure you: wrap them in PVC first. The same applies to needles and scalpel blades.

Boots are often cited as good hiding places for escape and evasion equipment, but beware. Walking is probably the only way you will be able to

## Selecting your equipment

The items you need to take are largely dependent on the environment you are going into, so you will need to make one up for each potential deployment area. In preparing your kit, choose things that can be used for more than one task.

You need:

1 First aid items
2 Signalling items
3 Water and means to obtain drinkable water
4 Fire starting equipment
5 Food and kit to help you obtain food
6 Shelter kit
7 Weapons

travel, and if your boots are uncomfortable or unable to protect your feet you will be in trouble.

## Step on it

If you have very thick shock-absorbent insoles in your boots, you can hide things beneath them, but check regularly to make sure the insole is not being worn away. Obviously only very thin items can be concealed this way, and nothing over about 8 cm long, as it may puncture the insole and your foot when the sole of the boot flexes.

### Survival rifle

A Ruger 10/22 silenced semi-automatic rifle, complete with folding stock and 4×40 scope, will definitely keep the larder stocked.

### SAS Belt Order

Sabre squadron troopers always carry E and E equipment as part of their belt order. This is not the definitive layout: individuals are allowed to carry what they like once they are on squadron.

 1  Belt, pouches and water bottles
 2  SLR magazines
 3  Rifle cleaning kit
 4  Purse net
 5  Fishing kit
 6  Snares
 7  Mess tin lid and rations
 8  Torch and filters
 9  Button-compass
10  Wire saw
11  Fire starting kit
12  Lock picks (note: these are illegal in UK)
13  Clasp knife
14  Prismatic compass
15  Miniflares
16  Millbank bag (for filtering water)
17  Field dressing
18  Survival ration
19  Heliograph
20  Silk escape map

# Survival

Condoms also need to be concealed with care: if they are unprotected the plastic wrapper will eventually wear and damage the contents, so when you come to use one in a survival situation it has a hole in it! Wrap them in PVC tape (ideally, a minimum of five should be carried).

If you can safely conceal a flint and steel firelighter in your clothing, so much the better, but make sure you know how to use it before sewing it in, otherwise the space is wasted.

## Compasses and maps

Small compasses are fairly easy to conceal and the small RAF button compass can even be swallowed and retrieved at a later date! However, these compasses only really give an indication of magnetic North, and are not accurate enough for bearings.

Rough maps of your operational area are not as difficult to construct as you may think. Pilots and Special Forces are often issued with elaborate maps, printed on cloth or silk and disguised as handkerchiefs or sewn into the lining of clothing.

## Major details

Your escape map should be a very simple affair, with only large towns, major roads, railways and rivers marked on it. Any other detail would be useless and confusing. Combined with your simple compass, it just makes sure you walk in the right direction. It is best drawn on rice paper or airmail paper, folded and wrapped in cling film or seran wrap and sewn behind a unit or rank patch or hidden under the insole of your boot.

*Above: Even if you are captured you should be allowed to keep your helmet and respirator, and the former can be pressed into service for cooking unless it is a new issue one.*

*Right: Three belt orders containing survival kit. Pistols can be useful but ideally you should not get into a position where you have to use one. The bottom set really needs a yoke to spread the weight.*

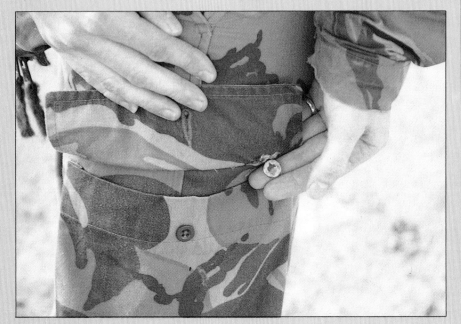

*Left: Useful things can be sewn into combats. The RAF issue button compass is excellent, and can be swallowed prior to capture and retrieved later. Also, some kit can be taped down behind your scrotum, and you can hide kit in your nether regions. Beware of injuring yourself if you use this method of concealment, and remember that, although inexperienced troops may not be very keen to search this area, your bottom will definitely be on the checklist.*

*Right: A Marine recruit builds a survival shelter on Dartmoor. Effective training, a minimum of equipment and local resources will provide the determined evader with all he needs. Inset: The commando wire saw in action.*

## Condoms can be used as:

**1 Water carriers**
Each one will take about 1½ pints. Remember to put the whole thing in a sock for support.

**2 Surgical gloves**
Bullet wounds are usually already highly contaminated, but if you are clearing out a wound put condoms on your fingers to reduce the chances of further infection.

**Signalling devices**
Useful for ground-to-air signalling: simply blow them up and place them on the ground in the desired pattern.

**4 Waterproof containers**
You can use them to protect kit or maps and for hiding things internally, and for keeping water out of weapons and radio equipment.

*Above: When you're searched by the enemy, the chances are that you will lose the most useful of survival tools – your knife. If you can successfully hide a sharpened edge of some kind, e.g. a razor blade, you can still make survival tools: it just takes longer. This fox was skinned with a flint flake. The sinew, extracted with a knife from along the back, is an excellent source of strong cordage for making tools: having to dig them out with your teeth is less pleasant.*

## Remember

**1** Every piece of kit you smuggle through the first search will help you escape.
**2** If they keep searching, eventually they will find everything.
**3** Make sure the piece of kit can be retrieved once you have escaped, e.g. that it is not so well sewn in that you can't get at it.
**4** Make sure you know how to use the kit you've hidden.

# Fighting Fit

The badge of
The Parachute Regiment

# What it takes to be a Para
# 'P' COMPANY Part 1

***When you volunteer for the Parachute Regiment you must pass a gruelling training programme before earning the right to wear the coveted red beret.***

As a recruit, your first 11 weeks consist of basic infantry training, not unlike that of the Royal Marines. During this initial phase you are introduced to a strange, new world; an existence totally alien to the one you once knew. To help you adjust, an eager team of dedicated instructors introduces you to the realities of military life.

You soon learn discipline. At the same time, you become noticeably smarter and accustomed to marching everywhere. You get fit. You learn the proud history and tradition of the Parachute Regiment.

## Learning your skills

As the weeks progress you are taught how to handle a variety of weapons; learn battle skills and fieldcraft; experience living in the field; and receive instruction on how to survive in a nuclear, biological or chemical environment. You are shown how

to read a map, and practise the correct use of signals and voice procedure . . .

On Friday morning of Week 12, the platoon suddenly enters a new phase when it is handed over to the permanent staff of P Company. Although your usual instructors are still with you, it is actually P Company that will decide your fate during the next five days of arduous selection training. If you fail to qualify at this stage you will be held back until the next platoon arrives.

P Company is designed to a severe

subjected to the usual warm-up exercises. The preliminaries over, the loud crack of a thunderflash heralds the start of the Steeple Chase.

You burst into a sprint, down a path ankle-deep in clinging mud. Before you is the first water obstacle. You leap into it. No matter how prepared you are, the icy water comes as a shock. It is *cold*! Try to ignore it as you clamber out of the pool, up onto the other side where another sprint quickly takes you along a wide track before turning off along another slippery, slimy path towards the second obstacle.

### Hitting the water

Again, the cold shock as you hit the water. Again, you fight your way through, up and out the other side and on into the woods. Now you are breathing hard, growing tired, but horribly aware that there is still a few hundred metres to cover before repeating the whole course again.

### Do it again!

The training staff seem to be everywhere at once. They pursue you remorselessly, shouting encouragement to those who are slackening. Almost impossible to imagine that these terrifying demons were once frightened recruits like yourselves. You slip in the mud and go sprawling. Before you can get to your feet a face appears, bellowing, just inches away from your own.

"Get up! Get up! MOVE!"

You scramble out of the mud and try to put on a burst of speed, but the NCO is apparently unimpressed. He suggests you run a little faster. By the time you've done the course a second time you're exhausted. But it's an exhaustion tinged with relief – you've completed the first real step along the road towards the red beret.

### The Log Race

Later that same morning you are taken to another clearing in another wood. Before you stretches a wide sand and pebble track. To one side are a number of heavy, wooden logs. As soon as the warm-up exercises end, the platoon, now broken down into groups of eight or nine men, waits for the thunderflash that will signal the start of another challenge: the Log Race!

Despite the weight of the awkward log slung between your team, the initial run-up is taken at a sprint. Each team vies for first place, the training staff urging you on. You're already tiring when you turn into a bend and

*Above and inset: The Steeple Chase is an arduous, wet and muddy course that you must negotiate twice in succession in under 16 minutes. When you've finished, the platoon is formed up in a single rank and awarded points depending on the time taken to get around the course.*

test of character. The 50 or so recruits are divided into three teams, each of which is actively encouraged to compete for the best possible time in a number of events.

### The Steeple Chase

P Company opens with the Steeple Chase. Concealed in a wood is a wet and muddy course, consisting of a long, slippery track and a couple of metre-deep water obstacles. For maximum points, you must negotiate it twice within just 16 minutes! First, though, you are led to a clearing and

*Above: Another exhausting trial is the Log Race, this time designed to test your team spirit, stamina and will to win. Eight- to 10-man teams compete to carry a cumbersome log around a 1½ mile course. For some, the strain is just too much.*

are suddenly confronted with a steep, sandy hill. Heavy rains have cut deep furrows into it and the sides crumble as you attempt to retain a foothold.

You lean into the incline, breath coming in short, stabbing gasps. Blinking the stinging sweat from your eyes, you struggle on. The cumbersome log is remorseless in its drag. Where the hell is the top of the hill?

### Nearly there

"MOVE YOURSELVES! COME ON! MOVE IT!"

The pace has slowed almost to a walk. Nearly there now. A man stum-

# Fighting Fit

bles. He regains his feet, staggers back to his place. The summit is reached at last. Veer left, along a straight stretch and then down a steep incline. Another man falls and is trampled underfoot. He goes rolling down the hill until a corporal grabs him and hauls him upright, encouraging him to regain the log. The recruit promptly collapses again, and is dragged along by the NCO. The officer in command of P Company runs past.

"Don't drag him! Don't drag him!" he yells.

In a daze, the recruit staggers to his feet.

### The last stretch
Finally, the last stretch. The pace is increased. Almost there. The finish looms closer. At last, after 1½ miles, you can slow down, get rid of the damned log. Each team closely follows the other in, until only half a dozen individual stragglers are left. For them, P Company is over. For the rest of you, there is still hope.

### Milling
The last period of the day is set aside for "Milling", which takes place in the gymnasium at Browning Barracks. Milling consists of each recruit spending one minute in the "ring" with another recruit of similar build to himself. Although boxing gloves are worn, it is not a boxing match.

### Showing your guts
It is a battle designed to instil aggression and confidence, guts and determination.

The recruits sit around on mats. Many faces show a distinct flicker of apprehension when a pair of medics wheel in a stretcher, with a medical kit laid out on top!

### Face the enemy
Each session opens with the opponents standing to attention in opposite corners facing the OC who, together with P Company Sergeant Major and a sergeant, overlooks the scene from the top of a makeshift platform. The contenders bellow their names to the major, turn and face each other.

### Fist and flesh
A bell is rung and the pair rush headlong into one another amidst a flurry of flailing fists. Gloved fist connects with bare flesh. A nose spurts blood. The fight continues regardless. A man goes down. The "referee" shouts at him to get back up. The recruits surrounding the battling pair

yell shouts of encouragement until finally the bell signals an end to the first match. Everyone applauds the effort. The next pair stand and the performance is repeated.

### Varying expressions
The expressions of each contender vary greatly. Most are distinctly hostile and dangerous-looking; some are blank, expressionless masks; and a few are downright petrified! It is a strange experience to attack a fellow recruit with no reason other than having been told to do it: some find it difficult to muster the necessary instant aggressive spirit.

The paradox of milling is that, while you don't want to hurt your mates, you've got to put on a good show to win their respect!

### Waiting for the bell
You know that the minute-long bout must inevitably end and so, when your turn comes, you do your best. You throw as many punches as possible and wait for that bell. When it rings, you know that you have finished Day One of P Company.

*Above and below: Milling is not quite Queensberry Rules. You are paired off for a one-minute bout designed to test your aggression and guts – the ability to instantly switch into action is an important attribute in your future career.*

# Combat Report
## Falklands:
# The Attack on Mount Harriet

**A Royal Marine from 42 Commando describes his part in the attack on Mount Harriet in the Falkland Islands, 11/12 June, 1982.**

For days we'd been sitting freezing our nuts off on top of Mount Challenger. The brigade was busy getting its act together: ammo was being brought up for the guns sited on Mount Kent. Intelligence and route recces were also on the go constantly, while we just sat and waited. The rations, the weather and the inactivity were all beginning to tell. Then we received our orders, and realised that although we were a bit apprehensive everyone was, in their own way, looking forward to it.

### The silence was shattered

The plan was to sneak around to the east and come in through the minefields at night, taking Mount Harriet by surprise! 'K' Company went first, followed by 'L' company. We were divided between them; I was assigned to 'L'.

We had two main tasks. The first was to bring up the rear of the three troops at the front, to supply supporting fire and help deal with casualties while they advanced. Our second task, when the attack was over, was to patrol forward and harass the enemy who, hopefully, would be fleeing.

We crept down off Challenger and into the gap between Mount Challenger and Wall Mountain. We were right out in the open, and I remember feeling very exposed. I could imagine the shells whistling down among us, and I was impatient to get moving again. It was only a short delay before we were off, this time following a cleared route to the start line.

We moved forward in a big snake, each man wrapped in thought. Occasionally we would stop and go to ground, with everyone wanting to know what was going on. 'K' Company were moving up to their start line. The plan was for them to go to the rear, and hopefully take the enemy by surprise. Our job would then be to assault the forward positions, which with any luck would be confused and breaking by that time.

The start lines were being secured by 'J' Company, the recce platoon of the Welsh Guards. There was an agonising delay while we tried to link up with our guides. Once we'd met up, they took our Milans off to find a good position from which to take out any enemy strongpoints encountered during the attack.

Suddenly the silence was shattered as our guns, mortars, and naval gunfire support were let loose on the slopes of Harriet. The noise was deafening, the effect devastating. We could pick out all the different sounds and where they were coming from. 'J' company was firing from Wall Mountain, a ploy to delude the enemy into thinking that we were coming from there. Then 'K' Company started their attack, getting quite close before they were engaged. We, meanwhile, watched in silence as all hell broke loose. Red, green, and white tracers were flying down towards 'K' Company. Everything was suddenly very scary and unreal. The Argentine artillery had now begun to open up from positions around Stanley. First a series of booms resounded in the distance. Then shells whistled past or cracked amongst the rocks near us.

When the signal came to attack we had to leg it to the lower slopes. The forward troops were already being engaged by sporadic firing. Now the artillery was aimed at us, scaring the hell out of me. The rounds being fired downhill at us were probably more dangerous, but you couldn't see them, just hear them crack by. The artillery was altogether different. You were up and running, and then when you heard the booms you hit the deck and waited for them to land. It was all around us by now, and the noise was tremendous. We were in a fold of ground – the boss, the GPMG gunner, and another two of us.

### They were hit by fire

We could just make out Company HQ coming up behind us. We legged it from our cover, and the HQ party dropped in behind us. When they got there, they were hit by fire. Both the signaller's legs were shot through. The rounds continued, stopped only by the Company 2i/c. I remember thinking, "Jesus, that was meant for us. Somebody must be able to see us". I was convinced that they were all aiming at me.

We kept moving in short sprints up the hill, listening all the time to what was happening up ahead. We could hear shouts as people took charge and directed fire. Their progress was hindered by machine-gun fire, which had to be dealt with before moving on. Suddenly it went quiet: a section commander was giving a fire control order. Everyone was listening, so when he shouted 'Fire!' everyone opened up. Someone fired a Milan on them, which we heard flying through the air, followed by a tremendous explosion, then silence. The machine-gun fire had stopped, and a ragged cheer went up.

### He was the commander

We pressed on. As we were nearing the top, the artillery fire seemed to intensify. I remember hearing the booms and diving down into a patch of shingle. Rounds exploded nearby, and the earth shook. So did I. Things were getting a lot scarier all of a sudden. I was convinced I was going to be hit. Then a flurry of small arms fire hit the shingle, and I was off. We finally reached the top and got in amongst the relative safety of the rocks up there.

While one of the troops pushed forward towards Goat Ridge, the troop we had closed with were settling down to look for prisoners and give covering fire. I had to go down the slope a bit to get a prisoner, an officer. He was just standing around in the open, watching everything. I grabbed him and sent him back up the slope ahead of me. At that moment we came under fire. A couple of rounds landed between our legs, and he dived for the only cover there was. I remember shouting at him and kicking him out of the way. The fire ceased, but the prisoner wouldn't stop talking about his brave men and our resourcefulness. We left him with the other prisoners to shut him up. It turned out that he was the commander of the unit defending Mount Harriet.

The troop on Goat Ridge now came under heavy fire, so we moved up to support them. The firing began to ease off as it started to get light. We sat around, checking weapons and each other, and waiting for orders. We treated our wounded first, then searched for food, prisoners and any souvenirs.

The attack was over. It had taken six hours, but Mount Harriet was secure. I'll never forget that night. I'm glad I was there, but I hope I never experience another night like it.

Here the OC briefs the platoon using a model of the area compiled from maps and air photographs, which gives the troops a far better mental picture of the ground.

# Fighting Fit

The badge of
The Parachute Regiment

# What it takes to be a Para
# 'P' COMPANY Part 2

*Following the shock of P Company Day One, the platoon is allowed the weekend off to recuperate — and to mull over the four days yet to come!* On Monday morning you fall in outside the barrack block, wearing fighting order and Bergen, and carrying your SA80: a total weight load of some 25 kg! The platoon is now down from 49 to 43 men. Ahead of you is a 10-mile speed march, or "tab", to be completed in less than one hour and 50 minutes – if you are to attain full marks.

P Company works on a points

system. Ten points is the maximum awarded for each event, and to qualify for your red beret you must strive for a total of at least 59 out of a HPS (Highest Possible Score) of 90 points.

### The 10-miler

The tab opens with a steady jog out of Browning Barracks. Once into the countryside, tarmac roads quickly give way to dirt tracks. In the summer these are usually baked hard, but in the autumn and winter the packed earth becomes a sea of soft, clinging mud. It sticks to your boots, adding to

the weight and slowing you down.

When not coping with the ankle-high mud, you are faced with tracks composed of coarse sand and pebbles, and the change from mud to pebbles and back quickly tires you. By the time you again hit a proper road it is all you can do to keep going.

Despite the relentless efforts of Recruit and P Company staff to keep the main body together, a number of recruits inevitably drop further and further behind. Some collapse and are immediately hauled to their feet by the training staff, who quickly

*Above and inset: The 10-mile speed march takes place along roads and across country. You're carrying a loaded Bergen plus your webbing, so it's quite a test of your stamina and determination. The aim is to finish as a group in under 1 hour 50 minutes!*

appraise the condition of the man to determine if he is shamming or not: the staff are expert at spotting genuine cases of exhaustion.

Usually the recruit can call upon reserves of energy to keep him going and, knowing this, the officers and NCOs will push a man to the limit if they think he has potential. It looks like rough treatment and it is, yet it is essential if some of you are to make the grade.

The 10-miler is both a physical and mental challenge. Obviously you need to be fit if you're to stand any

chance of completing the event. However, you must also condition yourself mentally and simply accept that you have to cover the required distance. Ignore the weight of your Bergen and the straps biting into your shoulders. Forget about the lump in your pack that has been rubbing your back raw for the last couple of miles. Forget the blisters. Just keep going.

### Points for finishing

When it does, only 18 of you finish together. You are within the time limit and so receive the maximum 10 points. For the others, who stagger to the finish, the number of points diminishes with each passing minute. They will have to do better on the other events.

### The Confidence Course

There isn't long to wait for the next one. Within half an hour of completing the tab, the platoon is marched across to the Confidence Course. This consists mainly of a series of walkways constructed from scaffolding, planks and wooden beams, and is set between 10 to 15 metres above the ground. There are no safety nets for those careless enough to fall!

Dominating the scene is the trainasium, a scaffold tower 15 metres high. This is topped by two horizontal bars set about three-quarters of a metre apart. Each of you has to walk along these bars, stepping over a small obstruction mid-way before halting and bending down to touch your toes!

### Leaping across

At the base of the trainasium is another scaffold contraption, topped by wooden beams and separated from the tower by a small gap. You have to cross this by leaping from a fixed point on the trainasium, and it's designed so that you have to jump *down* as well as across.

For most of the platoon the Confidence Course presents no real problem, but for one of you the short leap from the trainasium is just too much. Eventually he does succeed in crossing the gap, and the staff order him to do it a second time. He refuses, and the platoon is down to 42 men.

### Sixteen obstacles

After lunch you're marched across to the assault course – 16 main obstacles that must be negotiated three times in seven minutes.

The first time around tires you. By the third time, you're gasping for breath. A two-metre wall that presented no problem less than four

*Above: The Confidence Course is an apt description for this series of obstacles designed to test your ability to handle heights. Anyone who hesitates here isn't likely to jump out of an aircraft.*

minutes ago now becomes a formidable barrier. You're certain you won't make it. But you're wrong.

"GET OVER THAT WALL."

Surprising what a little gentle encouragement does. The staff assist you in negotiating the entire course for the final circuit, following which each of you reports to a timekeeper who awards marks according to your efforts. Another day is over.

The next morning, you're up bright and early. Two coaches take you to South Wales, where the platoon is to spend the next three weeks. There's plenty of room on the transport as the number of recruits is now 36.

*To get maximum points for the Assault Course you've got to clear 16 main obstacles three times in under seven minutes. The training team is on your neck all the time until you make it.*

After about three hours you enter Abergavenny. Towering above the town is a range of impressive hills. They are extremely high.

Shortly after passing through the town the convoy halts at the base of another mini-mountain. You quickly de-bus and, amidst shouts of command from the staff, hurriedly sort out your kit before lifting that damned Bergen.

## Steep march

Minutes later, you're marching up a very steep road towards the summit. You tab for 18 miles. Up hills. Down hills. Along the straight. Across country. On roads. The pace is relentless. Impossible ever to describe to someone who hasn't experienced it. By the time the platoon reaches its destination – Cwmgwdi camp – it's down to 33 men.

The following day a recruit is taken ill, further depleting the platoon. The rest of you begin Endurance 2, an agonising tab up Pen y Fan: at nearly 900 metres, the tallest hill on the Brecon Beacons. Needless to say, Bergens are again the order of the day.

The climb up Pen y Fan is horrendous. It goes on and on. Towards the top a terrific wind gets up, buffeting the straggling file of men. At the summit a dense fog suddenly closes in, bringing with it a damp, numbing chill. After a brief respite you set off downhill. The weight on your aching back presses down on your thighs and knees, and accelerates the onset of blistered feet.

At last, after an hour and a half, you arrive at the first tea-stop. A quick refreshment and then you're off across the 700-metre high Fan Fawr. When you finally reach the second tea-stop you're given time to cook a meal. Revitalised, you start on the final stretch – a six-mile speed march back to Cwmgwdi. At day's end, only 28 of you are left.

## Stretcher race

That night you fall asleep with cries of "Prepare to double" and "Double march" still echoing in your mind. You're up again at 05.00 hours. By daybreak the platoon is ready for the final event of P Company – the dreaded Stretcher Race.

This is probably the most demanding of all the tests: a seven-mile race, with two 14-man teams manhandling a 90-kg steel "stretcher" up and down steep hills (one with a 1:5 gradient continuing for more than a mile). Four of you at a time carry the stretcher, the others carrying your weapons until it's their turn.

## Slog to the finish

For once you are allowed the luxury of not having to wear a Bergen. Nevertheless, it's a long, hard slog to the finish. The previous week's events have taken their toll, and you're more exhausted than ever before in your life.

Yet you surprise yourself by completing the course. Sheer guts and determination, physical fitness, the will to win, and the all-important presence of training staff have contributed to your making the grade.

*Royal Marines yomp, the Paras tab. Ask a Para the difference and he'll tell you that tabbing is faster. At the end of the 18-miler, your feet are examined and some of you need your blisters syringed and injected – not a pleasant experience.*

Later that morning the platoon is transported to Dering Lines – "home" for the remainder of Advanced Wales. After lunch there's a short parade. No music, no fanfare. In a simple ceremony, each of the platoon's 27 survivors is awarded his prize for coming through P Company: the Red Beret!

*The final test, the Stretcher Race, is one of the toughest. Part of the seven-mile course is a hill that seems to go on for ever. By the end of this week, an average platoon might be down to 70 per cent of its original strength.*

# Combat Report
## Vietnam: FAC over Loc Ninh

**The 0-2 performed well as a Forward Air Control aircraft, but on average the Viet Cong shot down at least one a month in 1969 and 1970.**

**In November 1969 Doug Trumbo was assigned to the 19th Tactical Air Support Squadron at Bien Hoa as a 'Gimpy FAC' (Forward Air Controller), flying the Cessna 0-2 and supporting the 11th Armored Cavalry at Loc Ninh.**

I had been worried about how I would react to actual combat. But my initial feeling was one of irritation about being assigned to the peashooter 0-2. I'd been trained as a jet jock back in the States, and had had visions of blazing through the sky in a supersonic Phantom. When they assigned me to "in country" training in this prop-driven flivver, I felt insulted.

I soon discovered that an 0-2 pilot was closer to the "real war" than anybody in jets. Our job was to locate, identify and mark targets, so the jets could provide close air-support to our troops on the ground. I had to fly down in the bushes, navigating by the seat of my pants, and stare into the faces of the Viet Cong, who were trying to kill me just as I was them.

### I took the Cessna down

My first mission was unforgettable. Using a grease pencil, I jotted down distances and headings on the Plexiglas of the airplane – an easy way to keep information at hand. I cranked up the engines and took off, heading for a spot near Loc Ninh where the Cavalry was conducting a sweep to dislodge Viet Cong battalion. Pretty soon I had an Army lieutenant on the ground (Hard Rock), pleading, "We need your help, FAC. We're taking fire from a grass-covered ridge just north of the river."

"I'll check it out," I replied.

I took the Cessna down low enough to chase its own shadow across the green foliage. I flew over the ridge, peered down through an opening, and saw Viet Cong mortarmen feeding a weapon. They were as clear as day! My very first flight and I was eyeball-to-eyeball with the enemy! My heart was pounding as I called up a flight of F-105 Thunderchiefs who were nearby with ordnance.

"Hard Rock, this is Gimpy FAC. I've got four Thuds coming down the pike with nape (napalm). We'll take out those mortars."

"Roger that," said a relieved Armored Cav Lieutenant.

"They've already cost a couple of our guys."

To make sure you've really pinpointed the

**The 0-2 could carry two Minigun pods to suppress enemy ground fire. Targets were marked for the bombers with white phosphorus smoke rockets.**

enemy, and to keep him from getting away before the Fast Jets get there, you have to stay overhead and keep yourself in harm's way. I sucked in my breath and went over those VC mortarmen again. They were scrambling, knowing that my puddlejumper meant trouble. They were also shooting at me. Bullets whistled past, and I heard a thunk as one round hit my plane. I cranked the 0-2 into a tight turn and fired a smoke rocket at them as they ran for cover beneath the trees.

I directed the F-105s to bomb them. A jet acknowledged, came in, and dropped his canister of liquid fire.

"Fast Mover, this is Gimpy FAC. They're located about one nape length (the length of the napalm explosion) downhill from where you got 'em." The bastards were really shooting, but I didn't think the F-105 pilot needed to hear that.

"Can you try again?"

"That's roger, FAC. Coming in." The second F-105 dropped his napalm, which smeared the jungle just where the VC were running for cover. I circled overhead and watched the red-orange flames consume everything in their path.

"Gimpy FAC, this is Hard Rock. You got 'em!" A moment later, the lieutenant spoke with a sigh of relief. "Those bastards were causing us real pain. Thank you, FAC!"

### The war was always personal

Of course, you didn't always get a close-up view of the Viet Cong, and our own jets weren't always like the Cavalry, rushing in at the last moment to save the situation. Often you just flew over the jungle, looked down, and identified the bad guys. Sometimes the Fast Mover jets were so gruesomely inaccurate that their explosives or napalm missed the VC by half a mile. But the war was always personal in that plane. It was a rare mission when you didn't get hit. In fact, three guys in my squadron were shot down and killed.

How did it feel to be face-to-face with the enemy in war? My main concern was my ability to perform. Our troops needed support, and I had to prove that I could provide it. There were days when I flew with my stomach quivering from fear, but I always flew – even on the day when a 12.7-mm shell knocked half my tail off, forcing me to crash-land at Loc Ninh.

There were different kinds of enemy gunfire, all of them scary. The 37-mm stuff consisted of bright red balls that floated like balloons; they were fired in clips of seven, and a single hit from one of them would blow a little 0-2 to pieces. The 23-mm shells were yellow-white in

colour, and were faster. But most dangerous of all were the .51-calibre ZPU shells. They were almost invisible in daylight, and were potent because they had the highest velocity of all. In the 0-2 you flew in tight turns and hoped that they wouldn't hit you with anything big.

On one occasion, I was flying FAC for a patrol of Armored Cav troopers who'd been pinned down by North Vietnamese regulars. The bad guys were in caves on a hillside. I fired marker rockets, only to be hit by a spray of bullets that zonked out everything on my instrument panel. The 0-2 was still flying, so I used "dead reckoning" to keep myself in the air while guiding a flight of F-4 Phantoms to the target.

"Jesus, Gimpy FAC," radioed the guy on the ground, "You're smoking and dropping and spraying little pieces of yourself all over the place."

"I read you, Fast Mover. Now see if you can drop 'em three nape lengths north of my smoke. They're huddled under the trees but they're mean."

"Affirmative, FAC. You call, we haul."

The Phantoms came in a four-ship formation, and dropped 750-lb bombs directly over the NVA. The blast didn't look particularly impressive in the bright sunlight, but as I circled overhead in my plane I realised that we had caught a large number of North Vietnamese dead-centre. I had one hell of a time getting my 0-2 back to Bien Hoa that day – and no radio to use on final approach – but I landed shakily, satisfied that I'd done a good job. In the end I flew 234 missions, and each time the challenge was the same: get into the air, no matter how scared you are, think about the grunts on the ground, and get the job done.

**Trumbo's view of the damage from his Cessna 0-2. Fires are burning from the rocket strike and the ground is pockmarked with bomb craters.**

The badge of
The Parachute Regiment

## Advanced Wales: Week 1

| Period | Location | Detail |
|---|---|---|
| **MONDAY** | | |
| AM | Lecture Room | Lecture: Principles of defence |
| | Lecture Room | Lecture/films: Construction of a Battle Trench |
| | Lecture Room | Practical/lecture: Mine Warfare/Wiring |
| PM | Lecture Room | Lecture: Routine in Defence |
| | Lecture Room | Video: Effects of Artillery Fire |
| | Lecture Room | Lecture: Withdrawal |
| | Local Area | Road Walk and Run |
| **TUESDAY** | | |
| AM/PM | SENTA | Defence TEWT (Tactical Exercise Without Troops) |
| PM | SENTA | Withdrawal TEWT |

| Period | Location | Detail |
|---|---|---|
| **WEDNESDAY** | | |
| AM | Lecture Room | Lecture: Ambush |
| | Lecture Room | Video: Platoon Triangular Ambush |
| | Lecture Room | Lecture: Vehicle Ambush |
| AM/PM | SENTA | Practical: Ambush and Vehicle Ambush |
| **THURSDAY** | | |
| AM/PM | Local Area | Exercise Pegasus Trail |
| **FRIDAY** | | |
| 0800 | | Move to SENTA |
| AM/PM | D and X Ranges | Practical: CQB (Close Quarter Battle) |
| 1800 | Lecture Room | Video: Locating the Enemy, Take Cover, Section Attack |
| **SATURDAY/SUNDAY** | | |
| AM/PM | | Admin: Platoon Commander's Disposal |

# What it takes to be a Para
# "Viciously, viciously!"

*"Now you can put P Company behind you and get on with training for the reason that you're all here for. The worst is over: now it's time to start learning how to fight!"* With these words, P Company Sergeant-Major dismissed the platoon at the end of the stretcher race. After the rigours of P Company there is a sudden and noticeable difference in training.

There is a perceptible change in the attitude of the staff towards the recruits, whose time has now come to be moulded into paratroopers. You are now expected to exercise a certain degree of common sense and understanding: accordingly, the staff is not so quick to admonish those who are slow to grasp a point. After a lecture, you are given the opportunity to ask questions, and then it is assumed that you have understood the lesson and will not make a fool of yourself during the practical demonstration.

### Defence lesson

The following week opens with a day of classroom and outdoor lessons on aspects of defence procedures. The next morning you are driven to the huge ranges near Sennybridge to put into practice the previous day's theories.

### Digging your trench

After a tactical move into an area, the platoon is divided into several groups and tasked with preparing a First Stage trench. Much of the day is spent digging with pick and shovel. Later in the afternoon the groups are rotated between the training staff NCOs, each of whom will teach a different subject. Having found out the

The day's final lesson deals with the correct way to cover a trench with the Kit, Individual Protection (KIP) – an aid to defence against NBC fallout. The KIP is a sheet of nylon-like material which is laid on top of a nylon rope secured by stanchions, and criss-crossed over that part of the trench designated as the living quarters. Earth is then tamped down on top of the KIP, from the edges in towards the centre, until it is covered with 45 cm of overhead cover.

### Stone-throwing

The serious business of learning the arts of modern warfare is sometimes alleviated by moments of lighthearted banter. A favourite game (from the staff's point of view) is "Viciously, Viciously".

"Line up, lads, and pick up a stone. Right, viciously, viciously. Let's see stacks of aggression. First man, go!"

Right hand on hip, and clutching a stone in the left, you take your turn at running forward while screaming "Viciously, viciously!" at the top of your voice before hurling the stone with a mad cry. The exercise is designed to confuse and panic the enemy in the event of your running out of ammunition!

By mid-week the platoon is down another two men. One has opted to transfer to a "hat" unit; the other has made the mistake of going AWOL.

### Anti-ambush drills

The 25 survivors spend the day learning about ambushes. That afternoon you board three trucks and rehearse anti-ambush drills before setting off towards a harbour position. En route the convoy runs into a fourth,

*A little lighthearted background activity on the range, lobbing rocks at each other. The size of the rocks is carefully monitored by the NCOs.*

unexpected ambush! As the lead truck is about to round a bend along a forested track, there is a sudden whoomph as an explosion causes bushes to burst into flame. Simultaneously, other bangs erupt along the road, while from the cover of a densely wooded rise comes the crackle of small-arms fire.

You leap off the vehicles into the bushes on the opposite side of the ambush position, find some cover and immediately return fire. The section commanders take charge, shouting words of command, directing the fire and quickly creating order out of chaos. After a few moments you are

*A four-tonner hits a vehicle ambush. A trip flare burns and machine-gun fire rakes the killing ground as a section debusses to put in the flanking attacking while others return fire.*

*Above: Digging the four-man battle trench. A vast area has to be de-turfed to accept the spoil from the excavation and provide protection. Inset: Classroom work follows 'P' Company, providing some relief for injuries sustained – pulled muscles and rattled brains.*

hard way how to dig a trench, you are now shown how to run and operate a generator-powered drill, called a High Cycle Kit.

You are taught to erect a Type 4 barbed-wire defence and a low-wire entanglement. You will be shown how to set up a trip-flare and the M18A1 anti-personnel Claymore mine. Another lesson teaches the use of the Racal Field Telephone, the latest communication device for use in defensive positions: working off a land line, it can't be jammed and is considered especially reliable.

# Fighting Fit

ordered to cross the road, move up the opposite bank and fight your way through the enemy position. It takes several minutes to clear the wood. Six "enemy" soldiers are found. But your tactics are a bit clumsy, and it is obvious that there is still a lot to learn.

### Waiting in the rain

That night you move into another part of the forest and prepare your own ambush. Trip-flares are set, and you then settle behind your weapons and wait. And wait. It begins to rain, a trickle at first, and then a torrential downpour. The rain slowly seeps through your "combats", making them cold and clammy against your skin. Time passes and despite the rain, some of you have difficulty in keeping alert.

### Enemy sighted

At last there is movement along the track. You strain your eyes, wondering if it is just another night-time illusion. But no, there is a column of men moving from right to left up the muddy path. A flare is tripped, bathing the scene in sudden light.

Weapons burst into life, muzzle flashes flickering along the line of troops. After several seconds of intense fire the platoon commander screams "Stop!" This is the signal to watch, and shoot at anything that moves. One of the enemy tries to

*Above: After fighting through the enemy ambush position by fire and manoeuvre and reorganising, body searchers are sent back to search and check the position. Note that the searcher leaves his weapon with his oppo, who covers him while he searches.*

*Left: Setting a tripflare is a fiddly task. Here the tripwire is being attached to the spring arm, which means that the pot still goes off even if you cut the wire. Keeping your head below the level of the pot when you arm it is a good idea.*

crawl off into the bushes and is instantly gunned down.

"Stop!"

You cease firing and apply the weapon's safety catch. A two-man search party goes forward, quickly checking the "dead", with the aid of additional flares. They then rejoin the main group, and minutes later the ambush party silently withdraws, the ambush a complete success!

### Pegasus Trail

The following morning you are up early to take part in a day-long navigational exercise – "Pegasus Trail". Most of you succeed in crossing the 18 or so miles of hilly terrain in the allotted time. One syndicate however, resolutely refuses to move away from the roads and tracks. It arrives at each check-point hours behind everyone else. The staff are not amused.

### Fire and manoeuvre

The week ends with an interesting day learning Fire and Manoeuvre techniques. You put the lessons into use, using blank ammunition. Each rehearsal is followed by a question-

and-answer session, with the points drummed home again and again.

"Keep the rounds going down. It's no good pausing because the enemy, huddled in his trench, knows that a pause means he's about to be bayonet-charged. If you stop firing, the enemy will stand up and fire back and it'll be goodnight Vienna . . ."

"Move, up, dash, down, locate the enemy and kill him!"

"Keep the bounds short; three to five paces at a time so that you'll hit the objective in extended line at the same time . . ."

### Close Quarter Battle

You will walk through two Individual CQB Stances. One takes place in an open area with ample natural cover. The other runs along a narrow, woodland track. Other than range-firing, this is the first time you have trained with live ammunition. Pop-up Figure 12 targets add an element of realism to the exercise, the object of which is to move from point A to B, reacting as taught to the targets as they appear.

An NCO follows you closely, firing a sub-machine gun for effect if you fail to react fast enough. It is a safe but realistic exercise, and just the sort of action you joined the Red Berets for.

*Close-quarter battle with the SA80 is a good deal easier than with the SLR, and the percentage of first-round hits is dramatically better.*